CONTENTS

Preface

Acknowledgements

PREFACE

Many people have visited Walton-on-the-Naze and have found sharks' teeth and fossil shells on the beach beneath the Naze cliffs. A number of these visitors must have wondered how they came to be there, how old they were, and what Essex was like when these creatures were alive. Until now this information has been very difficult to obtain; no popular works have ever been written about Essex geology, and the subject receives little attention in natural history publications. This book, produced by the Essex Rock and Mineral Society, is intended to fill this gap and provide an account of the prehistory of the county up to the time of man.

Few people think of rock when they think of Essex, yet every landscape is built on rock of one or more kinds, from granite to the softest clay or sand. Each piece of rock is a store of prehistory. Even a pebble from the garden has its own story to tell. We therefore hope that this book will generate more interest in geology, the subject that investigates the foundations of our natural heritage. Although Essex has few prominent geological features when compared with most other parts of Britain, there is still much to see and this book emphasises the visible evidence of the county's geological past. Geology has been called 'the great detective science' and it is always best to examine the evidence for yourself first hand.

What started off many years ago as an idea for a slim booklet on Essex fossils has grown into the present work out of a desire to produce a book which would not only be of interest to the general reader, but also be a useful source of reference for anyone interested in natural history. So as to present this subject to as wide a readership as possible, some generalisations have inevitably had to be made and some geological terms that may now be considered outdated have been used. Comment or criticism will be welcome and considered for incorporating in any future edition. The text, diagrams and illustrations have been compiled from a large number of sources, many of them listed in Appendix D. Jargon has been kept to a minimum and when a new term is introduced it is printed in bold type.

For the purposes of this book Essex is taken to be bounded on the north by the River Stour, on the south by the River Thames, on the east by the North Sea, and on the west by the River Lea. It will be clear from this that we have chosen the old geographical borders of Essex before the local government reorganisation of the 1960s, and so include the present London boroughs of Barking, Havering, Newham, Redbridge and Waltham Forest.

Acknowledgements

I am indebted to Graham Ward whose text for an exhibition on the geology of Essex gave me the inspiration for this book and provided the basis for some of the early chapters. Graham, an authority on Essex geology, has also given advice on the development of the text particularly with regard to the geology of the M11 and M25 motorway excavations.

Particular thanks are also due to Stuart Adams, former chairman of the Essex Rock and Mineral Society, for help with the chapter on economic geology and also for his assistance and advice over a long period. In fact, without his enthusiasm and encouragement, the project would never have been completed. I am also grateful to Clive Walpole who was in charge of the graphic design and arranged the printing, as well as providing the line illustrations.

All the fossils illustrated are owned by members of the Essex Rock and Mineral Society, and I am grateful to Derek Breden, Brian Brett, Bob Burton, Jim Greenwood, David Turner, Joan Stubbs, Bob Williams, Clive Walpole and Graham Ward who lent specimens for this purpose. I would also like to thank Ed Oliver for drawing most of the tables and diagrams, David Bridgland who gave advice on Thames terrace deposits and Adrian Corder-Birch who provided information about Essex brick making. Also, special thanks to Ian Mercer and to David Manning who kindly read the manuscript and suggested changes which have greatly improved the text.

There are many other people and organisations who have given me valuable assistance, particularly those who have granted permission to reproduce photographs and illustrations. The extract from the Daily Telegraph on page 86 is copyright of the Telegraph Group Limited, London, 1997. The geological maps and diagrams - all of which have been specially drawn for this book - are based on maps published by the British Geological Survey.

Gerald Lucy

The Essex Rock and Mineral Society gratefully acknowledges financial assistance from Havering Arts Council with research expenses and from Stuart Adams with printing costs.

Chapter 1

RECONSTRUCTING THE PAST

Geology: the Great Detective Science

If you walk through the Essex countryside it is hard to believe that in the distant past much of the land you see was once covered by a vast ice sheet or that mammoths once roamed the county. Yet at an even earlier time the whole of what is now Essex was submerged beneath a subtropical sea in which sharks and crocodiles swam.

The study of these ancient times involves geology: the science that is concerned with the Earth. It deals with the history of our planet and the study of all natural processes that have affected it and, indeed, are still affecting it today. Some of the benefits of geological science are well known, such as in oil and gas exploration, but its study has many other social and economic benefits, most of which we take for granted.

Geologists learn about the history of the Earth by studying its rocks, which, to experienced eyes, can reveal a wealth of information. A visit to a quarry, for example, may reveal rocks full of fossils, the remains and imprints of animals and plants that have lived on Earth. The study of fossils and the layers of rock in which they are found can give information on the conditions that existed on our planet long ago, thus also helping us to understand the history of life, to predict climatic changes, and to look after the planet more successfully.

It is not only the professional geologist who can make a contribution to the science. Many amateurs in Essex have discovered new sites for research, or found fossils which have turned out to be species new to science. The general principles of geology are easy to learn, and the rocks beneath the Essex landscape have a fascinating story to tell.

Knowledge of geology can add greatly to the enjoyment of the countryside, whether one is in Essex or any other part of the world.

Geological Time

For the science of geology to be accessible the first thing to get used to is the vast periods of time that are involved. Geologists talk of *millions* of years in the same way that archaeologists talk of *hundreds* of years. It is useful to compare geology and archaeology because the amateur geologist is often mistaken for an archaeologist when he or she is found carefully studying a hole in the ground. An archaeologist studies the history of *mankind* through the excavation of human remains and objects either made or fashioned by man. Usually this involves only the last 250,000 years, for most of which man was using stone tools; it is only during the last 4,000 years or so that humans have been using metals. A geologist, on the other hand, studies the history of the Earth since its formation about 4,600 *million* years ago. To put this vast span of time into perspective, if we try to visualise 4,600 million years as 24 hours, the last 250,000 years of man's existence would represent less than 5 seconds! When one attempts to grasp this enormous time span it becomes clear that sufficient time has elapsed for great changes to have taken place on Earth.

Geological time is divided into **periods** just as English history is divided into periods such as Roman, Saxon, and Norman. These geological periods (and the sub-divisions known as **epochs**) are shown in fig. 1.

Principles of Geology

In an archaeological excavation the deeper one digs the older the finds will be. Medieval coins, for example, will be found beneath Victorian bottles, and Roman pottery in a still deeper layer. This basic principle of archaeology parallels two important principles of geology: firstly, that where there has been no disturbance each layer is younger than the one that lies beneath it, and older than the one that lies on top of it, and secondly, that it is possible to estimate an approximate date for a layer from the relics it contains. The same principles are valid whether we are considering human relics buried in layers of soil or fossils preserved in layers of rock.

It is, of course, common to find a layer (or **stratum** or **bed**) which is apparently barren of fossils; in which case it can be dated from the strata above and below it, or by comparing it with a similar fossil-bearing bed elsewhere. A laboratory technique known as **radiometric dating** (which measures the proportions of radioactive elements present) is used to calculate the **absolute age** of a rock in millions of years. From this the dates of the geological periods are derived (fig. 1). The study of rock strata, which is the key to understanding Earth history, is called **stratigraphy**.

Geological maps, which show the rocks that occur at the surface, can be purchased for most of Essex. Published by the British Geological Survey at a scale of 1: 50,000, they are of two kinds : **solid** maps, which show the rocks of pre-Quaternary age, and **drift** maps, which show in addition the Quaternary deposits such as boulder clay and glacial gravel (Chapter 8). It is thus possible to predict the rocks, and therefore the fossils that might be found, at any place in Essex.

Continents on the Move

It is now well known that the continents are not fixed in position but slowly travel across the globe on rigid 'plates' which fit together rather like a jigsaw and thought to move because of large-scale thermal convection currents in the Earth's mantle. The concept that accounts for plate motion is called **plate tectonics**.

Britain, together with the rest of Europe, has travelled north (at one or two centimetres a year) for hundreds of millions of years and was, at one time, well south of the equator. This helps to explain the presence in Britain of fossils of animals and plants whose descendants now live in tropical climates. Plates are slowly created by volcanic activity and destroyed by submersion into the mantle. This process continues today.

Rocks of the British Isles

Many of the rocks that make up the British Isles are **sedimentary** rocks. These were mostly formed by sediment accumulating at the bottom of a sea or lake and it follows therefore that almost all fossils found in these rocks are of marine or freshwater plants and animals. The sediments may have hardened (e.g. limestone, sandstone) or remain relatively soft (e.g. sand, clay); but they are all called **rock** by geologists. Remains of land animals will be found in these rocks only if their bodies were carried to the bottom of the sea or lake and then fossilised, which is a rare occurrence.

In certain areas **igneous** rocks are encountered. These rocks were once in a molten state and solidified either at or near the surface (**volcanic**) or more slowly at depth (**plutonic**). Basalt is a typical volcanic rock, whilst granite is a typical plutonic rock. Igneous rocks cannot, of course, contain fossils.

Metamorphic rocks are formed when any kind of rock has been altered by heat or pressure or both. Marble and slate are metamorphic rocks.

Sedimentary Rocks

The names given to many sedimentary rocks are self-explanatory and not only describe the nature of the rock itself but also identify the locality where it occurs most extensively (e.g. Thanet Sand). Sedimentary rocks are therefore largely classified according to their sedimentary character, or **lithology**. Geologists have divided some rock sequences into **formations** (e.g. the London Clay Formation) and often subdivided these into smaller units called **members**.

For some sedimentary rocks a more appropriate classification is one based on the fossils they contain. Because animals evolve over time the species present may be different in each layer and a series of **zones** has therefore been devised for parts of the geological time scale, each characterised by a **zone fossil** (e.g. the *Micraster coranguinum* Zone of the Upper Chalk). Zone fossils help geologists to identify strata and to correlate rocks in different areas even if they vary in lithology.

APPROX. AGE IN MILLIONS OF YEARS	ERA	SUB-ERA	PERIOD OR EPOCH	EVOLUTION AND CLIMATE
0.01	CAENOZOIC	QUATERNARY	HOLOCENE	The Quaternary 'Ice Age'
			PLEISTOCENE	
		TERTIARY	PLIOCENE	
25			MIOCENE	Age
			OLIGOCENE	of the
50			EOCENE	mammals
			PALAEOCENE	
100	MESOZOIC		CRETACEOUS	Age
			JURASSIC	of the
200			TRIASSIC	dinosaurs
	PALAEOZOIC		PERMIAN	
300			CARBONIFEROUS	Life appears on land
			DEVONIAN	
400			SILURIAN	The first vertebrates
			ORDOVICIAN	
500			CAMBRIAN	
1000	PRECAMBRIAN			Slow evolution of simple life forms
2000				
3000				Primitive life appears
4600				Formation of the earth

Fig. 1 The Geological Time Scale. The whole of the Earth's history has been divided by geologists into eras and periods as shown. These are of unequal duration and have not been drawn to scale. Note that the Precambrian Era, a time during which simple soft-bodied organisms slowly evolved in the oceans, accounts for more than 85% of the Earth's history.

Earth Movements and Erosion

Great changes are brought about by plate tectonics, by lesser earth movements, and also by changes of sea level relative to the land. Rocks which have been buried thousands of metres down may be brought to the surface and eroded by the action of water, wind and frost, the debris carried away by rivers to the sea, eventually forming further sedimentary rocks. Earth movements can create **faults**, which are cracks in the Earth's crust where the rocks have moved relative to one another. The sea may return and deposit more sediments after a gap of millions of years.

As a consequence of earth movements and erosion a region may therefore be a complex mosaic of various rock types of different ages: a record of the prehistory of the area over hundreds of millions of years.

Chapter 2

THE ROCKS OF ESSEX

The Land Beneath the Soil

T he surface geology of Essex consists mostly of a thin veneer of sands, gravels and clays (the 'drift') left behind by glaciers and rivers during the present Ice Age. These soft rocks could be regarded as the icing on the geological cake; a good analogy, as they contain some remarkable fossils yielding evidence of our most recent geological past. However, these rocks are the subject of the final chapter in our story (Chapter 8), and therefore do not concern us here.

The 'solid' rocks, those which would be exposed if all the drift deposits were removed, are shown on the geological map (fig. 3). For those unfamiliar with them geological maps can appear complex, but they are easier to understand if we imagine the landscape in three dimensions (fig. 4); it can then be appreciated how the underlying structure determines how the pattern of rocks appears at the surface.

Compared with many other parts of Britain, even the solid geology of Essex is young in geological terms (the oldest surface exposures are of Upper Chalk at about 80 million years); but much older rocks are present at depth and these are the beginning of our story (Chapter 3).

The Structure of Essex

Essex is situated in the London Basin which, as its name suggests, is an accumulation of sedimentary rocks distorted by earth movements into a broad trough-shaped fold; this is called a **syncline**. The northern boundary of the London Basin is the Chilterns and the chalk hills of Cambridgeshire and north Essex. The southern boundary is the chalk hills of the North Downs in Kent. Although this syncline is the dominant feature there are smaller structures within it which may cause local variations in the regional slope or **dip** of the strata. One of these is the Thurrock **anticline** (an arch-shaped fold) which causes the Chalk of the North Downs to come to the surface in south Essex. The Thurrock anticline is too small to be shown on the block diagram (fig. 4).

Several faults are known to occur, the main one extending from Chelmsford to Colchester and first discovered when a well was being sunk at Wickham Bishops. Movement along this fault may have contributed to the Colchester earthquake of 1884 (see box). An unknown fault some 7 kilometres (4 miles) beneath the sea bed off Harwich was responsible for an earthquake in 1994, which was reported felt by coastguards at Walton-on-the-Naze. Many of these faults only affect the rocks at depth and therefore do not feature on maps; these show only the surface geology.

The Colchester Earthquake

Although it is generally thought that earthquakes are rare in Britain they do in fact occur quite frequently. Approximately 300 are detected each year by sophisticated monitoring equipment and of these about 30 are strong enough to be felt. Occasionally, however, Britain is shaken by an earthquake which causes structural damage.

The most destructive earthquake ever recorded in Britain occurred in Essex on the morning of 22 April 1884 and strongly shook most of the county. It is known as the Colchester earthquake because the greatest damage was caused to Colchester, Wivenhoe and the towns and villages nearby. The tremor was felt over much of southern England and parts of France and Belgium, and its magnitude has been estimated at 5.2 on the Richter scale.

The number of casualties is difficult to estimate, but it is doubtful whether any deaths or serious injuries can be attributed to the earthquake. There was, however, considerable damage to over 1,200 buildings in Essex. The earthquake was probably due to movement along a fault in the ancient Palaeozoic rocks under Essex which would have affected the overlying cover of Cretaceous and Tertiary strata.

An extensive study of the effects of the earthquake was carried out shortly afterwards by the Essex Field Club and their detailed report, published in 1885, is a fascinating and extremely valuable account. Copies of the report are available for reference at Colchester and Chelmsford libraries.

Rock Exposures in Essex

Because of the maritime climate and the ease with which soft sedimentary rocks are disintegrated by rain and frost and become covered with vegetation, the only natural rock exposures to be found in Essex are on the coast, where the sea is continually eroding the rocks and creating fresh exposures. Inland, it is only when the blanket of vegetation is removed, for example when a major new road is constructed or a quarry or clay pit opened, that a 'window' into the past is created. Any excavation that is sufficiently deep to penetrate the topsoil will expose the rocks beneath, but it has only been possible to prove what is present at greater depth beneath Essex from boreholes sunk at various times in search of water and coal.

The Importance of Essex Geology

Geological research is continually increasing our knowledge of the subject and new theories are constantly being put forward to account for the origin of rocks and landscape features. In Essex, the deposits left behind by seas, rivers and ice sheets shortly before and during the present Ice Age are particularly difficult to interpret and the origin of some of these sediments is still unknown. The county possesses a great variety of deposits of this age (Chapters 7 and 8) and many of our geological sites are of great importance for research into this period of Earth history. The rocks exposed in the cliffs at Walton-on-the-Naze, for example, are internationally recognised as providing valuable evidence of climatic deterioration at the beginning of the Ice Age.

Many sites in Essex have increased our knowledge of animal and plant life much further back in time, during the Palaeocene and Eocene Periods (Chapters 5 and 6); and amateur geologists have made a valuable contribution here by collecting fossils from temporary excavations (e.g. road works).

The Shaping of the Essex Landscape

The surface features of the landscape or **topography** are largely controlled by the underlying geology. Although everyone would recognise a difference between the gently rolling countryside of north Essex and the flat coastal areas in the east, there are in fact five distinct regions: the Chalk region, the boulder clay region, the London Clay region, the Bagshot Sand hills, and finally the coastal areas and river estuaries. Each region has its own character with the underlying rocks influencing the vegetation, wildlife, land use, and even architecture.

The landscape has been shaped over millions of years by wind, rivers, glaciers, and marine waves and currents, and these processes are collectively known as **erosion**. The present day landscape of Essex is largely the result of erosion that has taken place during the Ice Age (over the last 1.6 million years); a period during which there has been remarkable variations in the climate. The study of the origin of landforms is known as **geomorphology**.

Essex through Geological Time

The following chapters have been designed to take the reader through geological time. The story starts with the ancient rocks beneath Essex, and continues through to the most recent deposits, those of the present Ice Age. In this way the reader can follow past events in a logical sequence and understand how successive layers of rock have been built up over millions of years and, very often, been partly or completely removed by subsequent erosion.

PERIOD OR EPOCH	GEOLOGICAL FORMATIONS IN ESSEX
HOLOCENE	Recent peat and alluvium
PLEISTOCENE	River terrace deposits
	Boulder clay and glacial gravel
	Kesgrave Sands and Gravels
	Norwich Crag
PLIOCENE	Red Crag
MIOCENE	No evidence in Essex
OLIGOCENE	
EOCENE	Bagshot Sand
	London Clay
	Blackheath and Oldhaven Beds
PALAEOCENE	Woolwich and Reading Beds
	Thanet Sand
CRETACEOUS	Chalk (Lower, Middle and Upper)
	Gault and Upper Greensand (beneath Essex)
JURASSIC	No evidence beneath Essex
TRIASSIC	
PERMIAN	
CARBONIFEROUS	
DEVONIAN	Shales and mudstones of Silurian and Devonian age occur at depth (beneath Essex)
SILURIAN	
ORDOVICIAN	No evidence beneath Essex
CAMBRIAN	
PRECAMBRIAN	

Fig. 2 Geological formations in Essex. The rocks that occur at the surface in Essex are comparatively young in geological terms.

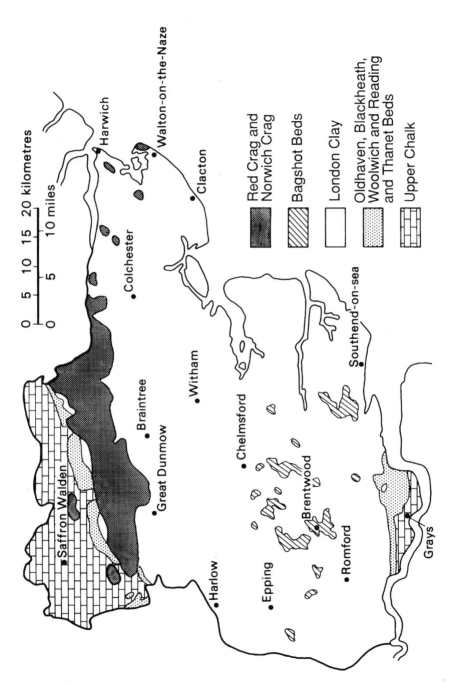

Fig. 3 Geological map of Essex (solid). The Ice Age or 'drift' deposits have been omitted.

0 5 10 15 20 kilometres

0 5 10 miles

Red Crag and Norwich Crag

Bagshot Beds

London Clay

Oldhaven, Blackheath, Woolwich and Reading and Thanet Beds

Upper Chalk

Harwich

Walton-on-the-Naze

Clacton

Colchester

Witham

Braintree

Great Dunmow

Saffron Walden

Chelmsford

Brentwood

Southend-on-sea

Harlow

Epping

Romford

Grays

16

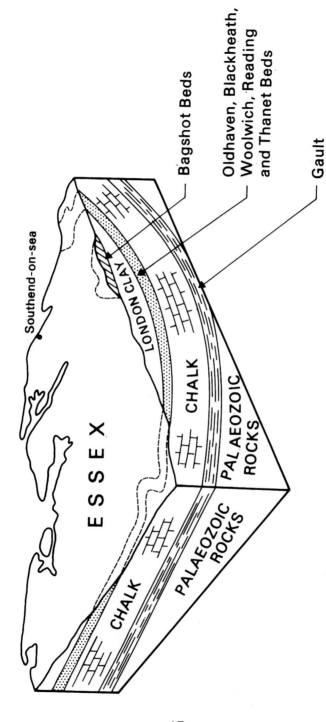

Fig. 4 Block diagram of Essex showing the structure of the county. An imaginary slice has been made through Essex from Saffron Walden east to Harwich and south to Grays. The dotted lines are the geological boundaries where they are present at the surface. The 'solid' geology only is shown; the Ice Age or 'drift' deposits have been omitted. For clarity the thin Red Crag and Norwich Crag have also been omitted and the vertical scale has been exaggerated.

17

Fig. 5 A fine brick mansion at Great Wigborough showing the damage caused by the 1884 earthquake. *(Photo: Essex County Libraries)*

Fig. 6 The ancient parish church at Langenhoe after the 1884 earthquake.
Many tonnes of stone fell from the tower into the nave and the roof was almost entirely stripped of tiles. *(Photo: Essex County Libraries)*

DISASTROUS
EARTHQUAKE
IN EAST ESSEX.

FALL OF THE SPIRE OF LION WALK CONGREGATIONAL CHURCH AT COLCHESTER.

LANGENHOE CHURCH WRECKED.

GREAT DESTRUCTION OF PROPERTY AT WIVENHOE, DONYLAND, AND MERSEA.

As we reported in a special edition of the *Essex Telegraph*, published within about four hours of the occurrence, Colchester was thrown into a state of indescribable panic and alarm on Tuesday morning by a shock of earthquake. The event occurred at twenty minutes past nine o'clock, and lasted several seconds. The ground was convulsed from one end of the town to the other, houses were shaken to their foundations, bells were set a-ringing, pictures dislodged from the walls, vases and ornaments on tables and cheffoniers overturned and thrown down, and hundreds of chimneys wrecked. It is impossible to exaggerate the feeling of consternation which prevailed. Everybody rushed into the open air, expecting to see visible results of the subterranean commotion and to be able instantaneously to divine the cause. Women shrieked in their terror and alarm in the most piercing manner, and strong men were utterly unnerved and paralysed. The revelations made in the succeeding five minutes only intensified the panic. It was first rumoured, and then ascertained to be actual fact, that the elegant and lofty spire of Lion Walk Congregational Church had been overturned and practically demolished. Master Herbert Johnson, son of Mr. Johnson, plumber, &c., Lion Walk, was standing at his door looking at the structure when the shock came. He saw the spire rent asunder, witnessed the air filled with the descending masonry, yet was so terrified that he was riveted to the spot, and at least one of the large blocks of stone fell at his very feet. A considerable quantity of the wrecked masonry fell clear of the Church itself and descended into the grave-yard, demolishing the tomb-stones, and converting the enclosure into a wreck. One of the ornamental lamps in front of the building was also smashed. Other portions of the *débris* fell upon the roof above the north aisle of the Church, and crashed through, causing fragments of broken slates to rain in all directions. At least from fifteen to twenty feet of the spire was toppled over, and the whole fabric was shattered to the basement. The effect of the shock seems to have been to lift the tower bodily on its southern side, and there is now a distinct inclination to the north of the rent and fissured building. Many of the stones at the point of detachment threatened at any moment to overwhelm

As may be imagined the office the centre of much enquiry, and Head-street was besieged with p sending telegrams to apprise fri the occurrence, nearly 100 despatched within about an details of the disaster that hand by midday on Tuesday we special edition on Tuesday, inc assurances from London that very slightly experienced there; there was very little ground for the current, inasmuch as the shock wa and did very little damage, though clocks stopped in many hous that the shock was so terrible tages were wrecked; from Poldon of Mr. Nelson was destroyed; fro the parish church was partially Brightlingsea that the shock w though little mischief was reported; serious destruction was caused cottages; from Marks Tey that t the form of two distinct shocks, consternation, which was not mu receipt of the telegraphic news of t chester; and that from all parts of dred there had come messages t truction of property, and indic of the area traversed by disturbance. There is no doubt t been productive of mental and ner such an extent as to be incalculable

Although little importance was a time, there seems little doubt that a was felt between five and six o' night, many persons thinking it w distant thunder.

It is stated that the earthquake *Echo* some three weeks ago, and t their faith to the adumbrations of a certainly be strengthened by th authorities predicted some such visi has caused panic throughout the w Division of Essex.

We may add that after the shock Railway Company sent a heavy eng in order to test the various bridge have been undermined or partiall the ordinary trains were allowed to

ANOTHER ACCOU

We also published the follow another source, in our special edit The terrible shocks of an earthqu certainly new to every inhabitant o land—were felt by the people of neighbourhood early on Tuesday earthquake shock, particulars of where, is, so far as we r in the history of the Borough as ha indeed, throughout the British Isle extraordinary occurrences are, fort rare. At eighteen minutes past nin

Fig. 7 A report on the Colchester earthquake in the Essex Telegraph newspaper of 26 April 1884.

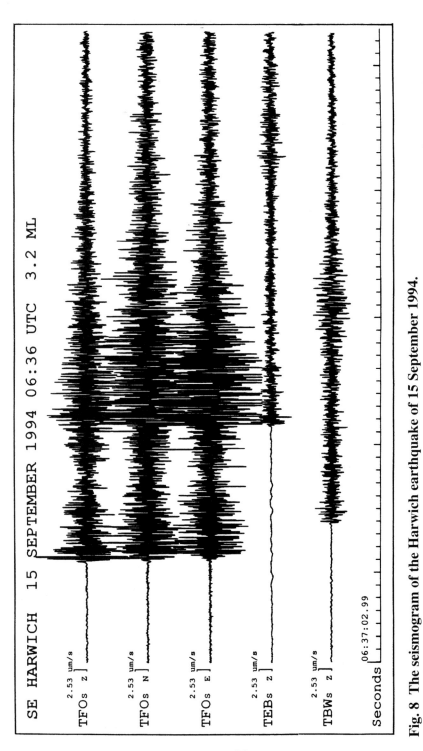

Fig. 8 The seismogram of the Harwich earthquake of 15 September 1994.
It shows the traces recorded by the automatic seismic monitoring stations at (from top) Folkestone (three traces), Eastbourne, and Brentwood. (*Reproduced with the permission of the British Geological Survey*)

20

Chapter 3

THE BASEMENT OF ESSEX

Hidden History

The oldest rock formation exposed at the surface in Essex is the Chalk (Chapter 4) which was formed between 100 and 70 million years ago; but what was Essex like before the invasion of the Chalk sea? The answer is found in the rocks deep beneath the county which are revealed in samples from boreholes and, where there are gaps in the record, by the study of rocks of similar age exposed in other parts of Britain.

The Oldest Rocks

The oldest rocks that have been found beneath Essex belong to the Silurian and Devonian Periods and are between 440 and 360 million years old. They consist of hard, slaty shales, mudstones and sandstones and are similar to rocks now exposed at the surface in the Welsh borderland. These old rocks, which have been encountered in Essex in deep boreholes at Harwich, Weeley, Beckton, Fobbing and Canvey Island, are over 300 metres (1000 feet) below the surface. During Devonian times most of Britain formed part of a large land mass consisting of a mountainous region to the north, and a vast plain of river sands and gravels (an **alluvial** plain) which stretched between South Wales and Essex (fig. 9). The climate was hot, and during this period the first animals began to colonise the land, having evolved from air-breathing fish.

Dinosaurs in Essex?

Beneath Essex there is a gap of about 250 million years in the geological record after the Devonian Period and we can only guess what Essex was like between the Devonian and the late Cretaceous. Any sediments that may have been laid down in Essex during this interval were removed by erosion before the next formation (the Gault) was deposited but the area must have been land for part of this time. This gap in the geological record includes the Triassic, Jurassic and early Cretaceous Periods (i.e. most of the Mesozoic Era) when dinosaurs were the dominant form of life on the planet. Remains of these giant, extinct reptiles have therefore never been found in Essex; although they would have lived in this area, any evidence for them having been eroded away.

The end of the Cretaceous Period witnessed the decline of the dinosaurs throughout the world. Beneath Essex, three rock formations exist that were laid down during this time: the Gault, the Upper Greensand, and the Chalk; each representing very different types of sediment. Although the Chalk is exposed at the surface in north and south Essex it contains, as we will see later, only the fossils of marine creatures.

The Search for Coal in Essex

The only way to prove which rocks are present deep below the surface is to drill a borehole, but this is expensive and therefore the location is carefully chosen so that it is likely to add to our knowledge of the sub-surface geology. This was particularly important during the Geological Survey's coal exploration programme in the 1950s when it was thought that Coal Measures (of Carboniferous age) existed in a concealed depression in the Devonian rocks beneath Canvey Island. This assumption was not unreasonable considering the proximity of a known concealed coalfield in east Kent.

Evidence for the existence of this depression came from measuring the variation in the force of gravity over the area and comparing this with an assumed average gravity value, thus producing a contour map with contour lines joining points of equal gravity. The map revealed a 'negative gravity anomaly' at Canvey Island (thought at the time to be due to the low density of Coal Measures sediments present in the depression) and in 1964 a borehole was drilled to test this theory (fig. 10). Instead of coal, low density rocks of Devonian age were found, but the borehole nevertheless provided a wealth of information, such as Devonian fossil plants, which helped to accurately date the sequence of rocks. The borehole was also the first in Britain to measure the direction and dip of sub-surface rocks by the use of sophisticated instruments.

It is an interesting thought that, had the borehole results been different, Canvey Island might have become a coal mining town; an example of how geology affects the character of the landscape.

The Gault Clay Sea

About 100 million years ago Essex was submerged beneath a muddy sea which deposited the **Gault**, a thickness of about 20 metres (60 feet) of stiff, grey, marly clay that rests directly on the inclined layers of Silurian and Devonian rocks. Although this formation underlies Essex it is only exposed at the surface in neighbouring counties; the fossils found there tell us that the Gault was laid down in a marine environment. An exposure of Gault on the Kent coast at Folkestone is renowned for its spectacular fossils, which have found their way into collections throughout the world. Flying reptiles called **pterosaurs**, with wingspans of up to 6 metres (18 feet), occupied the skies over Essex during this period; the fossil evidence for this has been found in rocks of approximately the same age near

Cambridge. After deposition of the Gault, sands spread into this sea to form a deposit called the **Upper Greensand** which has been found from boreholes to occur between the Gault and the overlying Chalk.

Sea levels had been rising throughout the late Cretaceous and in a few million years this was to lead to widespread flooding of the continents - the next chapter in the geological history of Essex.

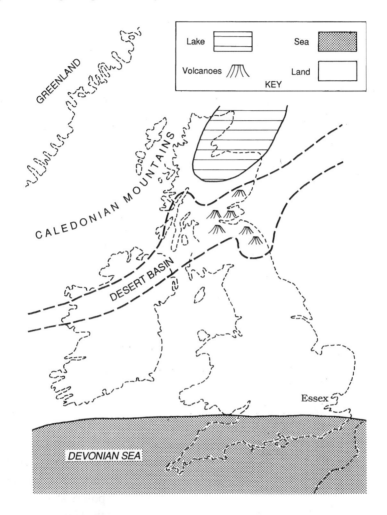

Fig. 9 The geography of Britain during Devonian times (approximately 370 million years ago). Essex was part of a low-lying area between the mountains and the sea, occasionally being flooded as the coastline changed position. Sandstones and mudstones of Devonian age occur at depth beneath most of Essex. Britain at this time lay just south of the equator and the Atlantic Ocean did not exist.

23

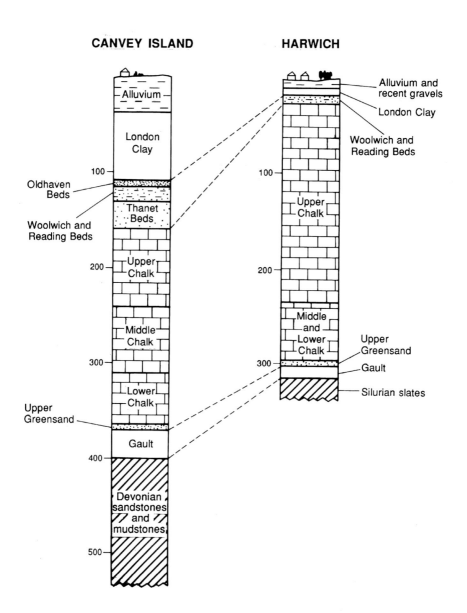

Fig. 10 The geological succession (drawn to scale) encountered in the Canvey Island and Harwich boreholes.

The illustration clearly shows the variation in thickness of each geological formation across the county. The depth (in metres) below ground level is shown on the left of each succession.

24

Chapter 4

THE CHALK SEA

A Rise in World Sea Levels

Between 100 and about 70 million years ago, after deposition of the Upper Greensand, world sea levels continued to rise until almost all of Britain and northern Europe was submerged beneath a tropical sea. At this time there was probably no ice at the Earth's poles and sea levels were up to 300 metres (1000 feet) higher than those today. Shorelines were far away from Essex, which meant that the water was remarkably pure and the 'mud' that accumulated on the sea floor consisted almost entirely of the fragmented hard parts, or **coccoliths**, of microscopic marine algae (fig. 12). Up to 500 metres (1,600 feet) of this pure white calcium carbonate 'mud' was deposited over a 30 million year period and it became the soft, white, friable limestone that we call **chalk**.

There are three divisions of the Chalk formation - **Lower, Middle** and **Upper** - but only the Middle and Upper divisions occur at the surface (or **crop out**, as geologists say) in Essex, and the Middle Chalk only in the extreme north-west of the county. Beds of hard, nodular chalk occur at certain levels and these contain fossils that indicate deposition of the sediment in a shallow sea; but most of the Chalk is believed to have been deposited in fairly deep water. Although a considerable thickness of chalk is present under south-east England, the average rate of deposition must have been extremely slow. Some geologists have estimated this to have been as little as one centimetre (less than half an inch) every 1000 years.

As a result of plate tectonics the Atlantic Ocean was slowly forming to the south, but Britain and North America had not yet separated.

Life in the Chalk Sea

The sea during this time was also home to many larger creatures, whose fossilised remains can be found embedded in the Chalk. The most common of these fossils that can be found in the Chalk of Essex are echinoids (sea urchins), which were bottom-dwelling scavengers. Like modern sea urchins their shells were covered with spines which served to protect the animal against predators during life but parted from the shell after death. The heart-shaped echinoid *Micraster* (fig. 15) is a well known chalk fossil.

The Chalk sea was alive with many other invertebrates, but the only ones to be commonly preserved in the Upper Chalk are bivalves (a class of mollusc which includes cockles, mussels, clams and oysters), brachiopods (another type of shellfish), crinoids (sea lilies), sponges and corals. Teeth of various kinds of fish, including sharks, are also found. The shells of gastropods (a class of mollusc which includes snails, whelks and limpets), ammonites (extinct molluscs with coiled, chambered shells) and some species of bivalve were made of a different form of calcium carbonate and therefore dissolved and not preserved as fossils.

At the top of the food chain in the Chalk sea were giant marine reptiles known as mosasaurs which were up to 10 metres (33 feet) long and must have been formidable predators. A mosasaur had a long body and tail, paddle-like limbs and heavy jaws armed with sharp conical teeth. Most of the mosasaur remains from the English Chalk are fragmentary; the fossils from Essex include isolated teeth found by quarry workers at Grays in the nineteenth century.

Flints

Nodules of silica (silicon dioxide) in a very finely crystalline state occur in layers in the Upper Chalk and these are called **flints**. The silica came from the skeletons of sponges which were dissolved by sea water trapped in the limy mud; the silica was then precipitated as flint nodules at certain levels, mainly in burrows made by marine animals.

When freshly dug from the Chalk, flint nodules are commonly black or dark grey in colour with a white outer rind or cortex (fig. 16). They can be of the most remarkable shapes, often with spiky protrusions; and sometimes they can be ring-shaped structures. For this reason they are often mistaken for the fossils of all sorts of bizarre creatures and are known as 'pseudo-fossils'. Flint is very tough but it fractures to produce razor-sharp fragments with a characteristic 'conchoidal' fracture surface, so called because it resembles the surface of a shell. Flint was of great importance in human development for the manufacture of tools and for making fire.

Many fossils in the Chalk, particularly echinoids, are found to be infilled with or enclosed by flint. With a little experience it is fairly easy to distinguish a genuine fossil from a pseudo-fossil but mistakes can still be made, particularly with banded flints, which are quite common and do not appear to have an organic origin. Echinoids are of particular interest because when the shell is removed using dilute acid the flint surface beneath often reveals fine details of the underside of the shell. Flints often contain fossil sponges which are usually preserved as irregular hollow cavities in flint nodules; when broken open these nodules sometimes contain a white powder known as 'flint flour' which contains sponge fragments and microscopic fossils of tiny animals that lived on the sponge during its life.

Occasionally, cavities lined with sparkling crystals of transparent **quartz** (another form of silica) are found in flint, but these are rare.

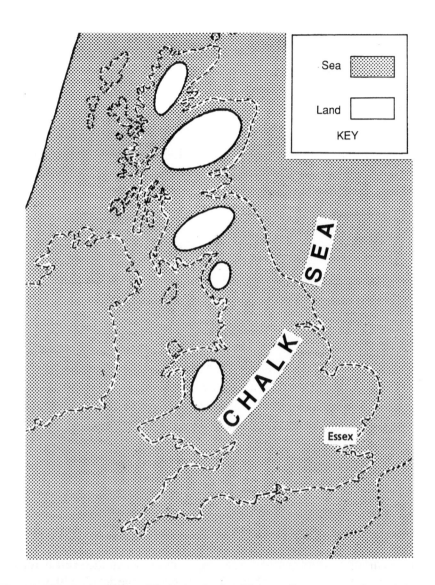

Fig. 11 The geography of Britain during Upper Cretaceous times (approximately 85 million years ago).

While the last of the dinosaurs roamed across North America, almost all of Britain lay beneath a deep tropical sea. The water contained very little sediment, depositing a soft, pure, fine-grained limestone known as chalk which now underlies the whole of Essex. It was during the Cretaceous Period that Europe started to split away from North America.

27

A World in a Piece of Chalk

Chalk is almost entirely made up of coccoliths, tiny disks or plates of calcium carbonate that formed the protective covering of microscopic marine algae. These coccoliths fell to the sea floor like continuous snow fall to form the white mud that was eventually to become chalk.

Chalk therefore consists almost entirely of fossils but they are so small that only with the aid of an electron microscope is it possible to see them. Even the white dust that soils your fingers as a result of examining a piece of chalk will be made up of millions of these tiny fossils. When doing this be sure to use the real thing; modern blackboard chalk is not chalk at all, it is made from the mineral gypsum.

Fig. 12 Coccoliths can be clearly seen in this highly magnified image of a piece of chalk produced by an electron microscope. Each coccolith is only about 1/200 millimetre (1/5000 inch) in diameter. *(Photo provided by J. M. Hancock)*

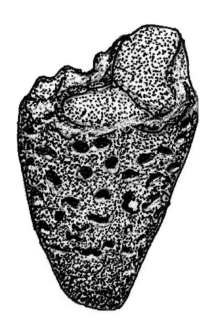

Fig. 13 The sponge *Siphonia koenigi* preserved in flint.
From Ice Age gravels at Chadwell St. Mary, near Grays,
derived from the Upper Chalk.

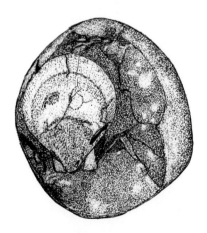

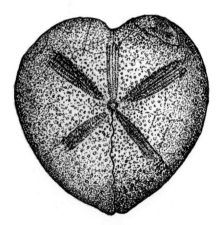

Fig. 14 The bivalve *Chlamys cretosa* preserved as a mould in a pebble of flint. From Ice Age gravels at Stanway, near Colchester, derived from the Upper Chalk.

Fig. 15 The echinoid or sea urchin *Micraster*. From a quarry in the Upper Chalk near Grays.

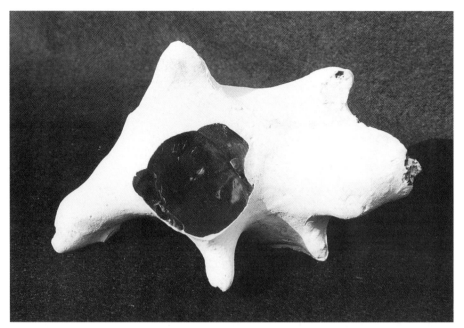

Fig. 16 A typical flint nodule from the Upper Chalk showing the black core and white cortex. *(Photo: G. Lucy)*

Fig. 17 A disused chalk quarry near Purfleet.
Note the horizontal layers of flint nodules. *(Photo: G. Lucy)*

30

Finding Chalk Fossils

Chalk fossils are popular with collectors because they are often perfectly preserved and, although not common, can be easily collected, cleaned and prepared.

In Essex, fossils can be found in virtually any Chalk exposure but finding them requires some experience as they are nearly the same colour as the host rock. There are large disused quarries in the vicinity of Grays and Purfleet which produced some magnificent fossils during their working life; but access may be restricted nowadays and permission should always be sought before entering. Many of these old quarries are flooded, with high vertical faces, thus providing safe havens for wildlife as well as being of geological and historical interest. Unfortunately the value of these sites is not always appreciated and many of the faces are threatened by landscaping.

In the north of the county several old small pits in the Upper Chalk near Saffron Walden have also yielded specimens, and many Chalk fossils were found during the excavation of cuttings for the M11 motorway.

Waterworn flint pebbles, derived from the Upper Chalk, can be found throughout Essex and these often contain fragments or traces of fossils (fig. 14).

The Great Extinction

Zone fossils indicate that in Essex the uppermost part of the Upper Chalk is missing. A considerable time interval must therefore have elapsed between deposition of the highest zone of the Upper Chalk in Essex (the *Micraster coranguinum* zone) and the succeeding Thanet Sand. During this interval (perhaps about 10 million years) Essex must have been land resulting in the highest zones of the Chalk being removed by erosion.

Great changes were now taking place in life on Earth; the end of the Mesozoic Era, 65 million years ago, spelled extinction not only for dinosaurs and the giant marine reptiles, but for millions of other creatures including the ammonites. Geologists are still debating the reason for this marked change in the fauna of our planet, a time when up to half of all living species may have become extinct. The impact of a giant meteorite may be part of the explanation.

Since the end of the Mesozoic Era the sea has returned many times and the countless millions of flint nodules from the eroded zones of the Chalk have been ground down to sand and pebbles by the relentless pounding of the waves. This material has been redeposited creating many of the rock formations described in the following chapters.

Chapter 5

SWAMPS AND ESTUARIES

The Thanet Sand

In Essex, erosion continued into the Tertiary Era until, about 60 million years ago, the county was submerged beneath a shallow sea. Great quantities of fine sand were brought into this sea from the adjoining land to form up to 30 metres (100 feet) of yellowish brown **Thanet Sand** which lies directly on the Upper Chalk.

A substantial thickness of Thanet Sand can be seen resting on Upper Chalk in many of the old chalk pits near Grays and it has been proved by borehole records to extend northwards beneath central Essex to be revealed again in the old chalk pits near Sudbury. No fossils have been found in the Thanet Sand in Essex, but marine shells have been obtained from this formation in Kent.

The junction between the Chalk and the Thanet Sand is marked by a distinctive layer of green-coated flints in a sandy clay called the **Bull Head Bed**. The bed is so called because the flints it contains are not rounded and still have their protrusions or 'horns', just as they came out of the Chalk. This junction, which is very visible in the Grays chalk pits, is the Cretaceous/Tertiary boundary - the point at which the mass extinction took place throughout the world. The actual time of the extinction is not recorded in these rocks as the topmost beds of the Chalk are missing; nevertheless the junction still marks one of the most important events in the history of the Earth.

The Woolwich and Reading Beds

Following deposition of the Thanet Sand, the sea became shallower with lagoons and estuaries in Essex depositing extremely varied types of sediment. These deposits are traditionally known as the **Woolwich and Reading Beds** and in Essex they consist of three contrasting types of sediment reflecting the geography of the county during the time of deposition.

In the south of Essex the lower, marine part of the Woolwich and Reading Beds (traditionally known as the **Woolwich Bottom Bed**), consists of a pebble bed, green loams and sands with pebble seams, which pass up into yellow sands laid down in a lagoon. Woolwich pebble beds and sands are currently visible in a quarry near Orsett (fig. 20). A seam of **lignite** (a type of coal), which indicates emergence and growth of vegetation, is known to occur between Aveley and Stifford; this was well-exposed during excavations for the M25 motorway.

The lignite seam is overlain by typical Woolwich beds - sand and stiff shelly clays - which contain a restricted range of fossils. Bivalves such as the oyster *Ostrea bellovacina*, and gastropods such as the whelk *Brotia melanoides* (fig. 19) occur, indicating estuarine conditions. Freshwater gastropods in thin seams in the shelly clays have been found at Aveley and Leytonstone and indicate temporary freshwater conditions on the dominantly brackish mudflats. In the north and west of Essex, these clays pass laterally into unfossiliferous river sediments, the typical Reading Beds.

Sarsens and Puddingstones

Throughout Essex can be found giant boulders, some hidden in grass verges or churchyards, others standing upright by farm gates or at road junctions. Many of these stones were of religious importance to early man and there are still myths and legends about them; but how were they formed, and how did they become so widely scattered across the county?

Their origin appears to be the sands and pebble seams of the Reading Beds which at some stage must have been exposed at the surface when the climate of Essex was extremely hot and dry (probably during the Miocene Period some 20 million years ago). During that time, water with dissolved silica was drawn to the surface and the sands and pebble beds became cemented by silica (in the form of quartz) to form tough sandstones and conglomerates. Subsequently, when these beds were subjected to erosion and broken up, large blocks of the hard rocks remained and these were scattered by glaciers and rivers during the present Ice Age.

The sandstone boulders are known as **sarsens**, a name that originated in Wiltshire where they occur on the chalk downland (many of the massive stones of Stonehenge are sarsens). They are very common in Essex and are often seen set in the ground as landmarks or built into walls, particularly in the north-west of the county. Some of the best known sarsens are probably those in the High Street and churchyard at Ingatestone. Sarsens found on the eroded chalk surface in the Grays area are the most remarkable of all. These are usually unweathered and exhibit curious features on the surface (fig. 21) which may be casts formed by the original sand infilling hollows on a muddy sea bed, or they could have been formed by differential sinking of the sand into soft mud that was formerly underneath.

The conglomerate is called **Hertfordshire puddingstone** after the county where it occurs as a layer in some quarries, and after its resemblance to a plum pudding. It is made up of well-rounded flint pebbles up to 5 centimetres (2 inches) in diameter in an extremely hard quartz-cemented matrix (fig. 22). Puddingstone should not be confused with the other cemented gravels; in the case of puddingstone the pebbles and the enclosing matrix are the same hardness, therefore when a piece of puddingstone is broken the plane of fracture passes through rather than around the pebbles.

Puddingstone must be one of the most instantly recognisable rocks; when cut and polished it can also be one of the most attractive, having a great variation in colour (brown, red, yellow, orange and pink have been known, and the pebbles often have zones of different colours). Because it takes a high polish it has been turned into decorative items (an example being Georgian snuff boxes) and fine pieces of jewellery; it is still so used today. Puddingstone has also been traded around the world; it was reported that a specimen was on display in the gemstone collection of the Hermitage Museum in St. Petersburg.

In north and central Essex puddingstone occurs as boulders at many roadside locations (fig. 23) but smaller pieces turn up in gravel pits or on the surface of ploughed fields. It has been the subject of many superstitions, one of which was that it grew in the soil, hence the name 'growing stone'. This belief has led to fine examples being destroyed out of fear that they might eventually block rivers or destroy crops. Puddingstone has had practical uses, particularly in Roman times when its great hardness made it useful for making querns for grinding corn (Saffron Walden Museum has a puddingstone quern on display that visitors can actually use to produce flour from corn supplied). Stone Age man also knew of puddingstone - in Colchester Castle Museum is a puddingstone hand axe from Braintree.

The Blackheath and Oldhaven Beds

The **Blackheath Beds** are pebble beds which occupy deep channels cut right through the underlying Woolwich and Reading Beds. They occur in southeast London and Kent and may be present in the extreme south-west corner of Essex, but are not there exposed at the surface. The most famous Blackheath Beds locality is the sand pit at Abbey Wood in south-east London which has yielded a large number of fossils.

Of the same age as the Blackheath Beds are the **Oldhaven Beds** which are mostly sands but also contain well-rounded flint pebbles, especially at the base. They crop out in the south of Essex but are exposed only in temporary excavations where they are found to be rarely more than 3 metres (10 feet) thick. In places they contain shell seams which yield a distinctive fossil assemblage. Bivalves such as the cockle *Glycymeris plumstediensis*, gastropods such as the whelk *Pseudoliva fissurata*, and the teeth of the sting ray *Hypolophus sylvestris* are typical Oldhaven Beds fossils. The Oldhaven Beds also contain an abundance of shark and fish teeth and bones.

Parts of the Oldhaven Beds are cemented by calcium carbonate into hard masses of sandstone which make the more fragile shells easier to recover intact

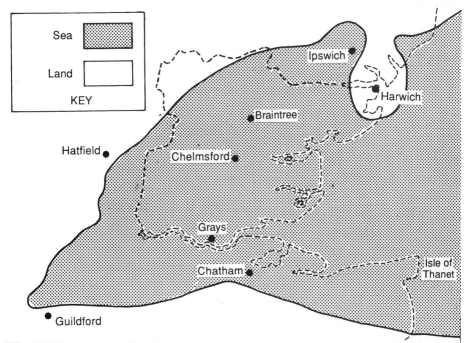

Fig. 18 The geography of south-east England during early Palaeocene times (approximately 60 million years ago). The shallow sea that occupied the Essex area deposited the Thanet Sand directly on top of the Chalk. The coastline is based on the present day extent of the Thanet Sand but it is likely that the sea occupied a greater area, the evidence for this having been removed by later erosion.

Fig. 19 Gastropods from the Woolwich Beds at Aveley. *(Photo: G. Lucy)*

35

Fig. 20 Detail of the Woolwich Beds in Orsett Depot Quarry, near Orsett.
Cutting vertically across the bedding is the sand-filled burrow of a shrimp. This
burrow is known as a **trace fossil** and was made some 60 million years ago when
these sands were being laid down on a sea bed. The scale is given by the
geological hammer. *(By permission of the Director, British Geological Survey.
Copyright NERC)*

Fig. 21 A sarsen stone at South Ockendon. *(Photo: G. Lucy)*

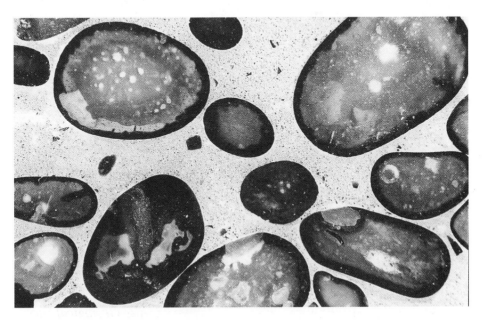

Fig. 22 A polished slab of puddingstone. *(Photo: G. Lucy)*

37

Fig. 23 A boulder of puddingstone near Newport. Similar boulders can be seen on the roadside at many locations in Essex. *(Photo: G. Lucy)*

Fig. 24 A block of sandstone from the Oldhaven Beds containing a large number of fossil shells. Found in 1979 during excavations for the M25 motorway at Aveley. *(Photo: G.R. Ward)*

Fig. 25 Detail of another block of shelly sandstone from the Oldhaven Beds at Aveley. It is remarkable that this represents part of an ancient sea floor that covered Essex about 60 million years ago. *(Photo: G. Lucy)*

(figs. 24 and 25). A temporary section through the Oldhaven Beds was exposed in excavations for the M25 motorway at Aveley where, although less than one metre (3 feet) thick, the richly fossiliferous shell seams yielded over 60 species, including a bone of the earliest bird to be found in Essex. In the north of the county the lateral equivalent of the Oldhaven Beds (formerly called the **London Clay Basement Bed**) consists of fossiliferous silty clays. These clays crop out in the north-west and north of Essex and were seen in 1979 in a temporary pit adjacent to the M11 motorway at Elsenham.

Sea level was now rising and Essex was slowly being submerged beneath the London Clay sea (the subject of the next chapter). A pebble bed exists (known as the **Suffolk Pebble Bed**) which represents a beach as the sea covered more and more of the land. This pebble bed underlies north-east Essex and is exposed along the River Deben in Suffolk where it yields sharks' teeth, molluscs and rare mammal remains.

Recent Research

The rocks described in this chapter are a complex series of deposits and the different names used can be confusing. To make matters worse, recent research has resulted in new terms being introduced such as the Upnor Formation (the Woolwich Bottom Bed) and the Harwich Formation (the Blackheath Beds/Oldhaven Beds/London Clay Basement Bed) and these will be found in modern geology textbooks. For our purposes it is sufficient to describe these rocks (i.e. those between the Chalk and the London Clay) as sands, clays, pebble and shell beds laid down by rivers, estuaries and shallow seas on the eroded surface of the Chalk.

As there are very few permanent exposures, our knowledge of these rocks has been obtained largely from temporary sections such as the M11 and M25 motorway cuttings where Graham Ward and a team of amateur geologists carried out much work. Amateur geologists have an important role in discovering and recording such sections before they are lost forever. Without their detective work we would know a lot less about the landscape and wildlife of Essex during this early part of the Tertiary Era.

Chapter 6

PALM TREES AND CROCODILES

A Subtropical Climate

During the early part of the Eocene Epoch about 55 million years ago southern England had a subtropical climate and the area that was to become Essex was submerged beneath a warm sea, up to 200 metres (600 feet) deep. The shoreline, which could have been as far away as the Midlands (fig. 27), supported a subtropical rain forest with plant species related to the mangroves. Similar coastal areas are now found in present day Indonesia and Malaysia. Rivers flowed into this sea bringing mud and silt which settled and became compacted, eventually to form a thickness of up to 150 metres (500 feet) of clay called the **London Clay**. During this period Essex was situated around latitude 41°, the same as present day Naples.

The London Clay

The London Clay is a stiff and sometimes silty, blue-grey clay, sandy near the base and with sand seams towards the top, which has weathered to a brownish colour near the surface. It crops out over most of Essex and contains layers of **septarian nodules**, claystone concretions that are so called because internally they contain radiating, mineral-filled cracks or 'septa'. Numerous small concretions of calcium phosphate called **phosphatic nodules** are also common at some levels. The septarian nodules, also known as 'cement stones', were formerly collected from the coast for use in the manufacture of cement (Chapter 9). The lower portion of the London Clay contains seams rich in volcanic ash which fell into the London Clay sea; at this time there were active volcanoes in western Scotland (as a result of the opening of the North Atlantic Ocean), and probably others nearer to Essex, off the coast of Denmark. Several hard beds of cement stone occur within the clay along the River Stour and on the beach at Harwich, which contain minute fragments of volcanic glass from these eruptions; the most prominent of these is called the **Harwich Stone Band**. This lowest part of the London Clay is included in the Harwich Formation (referred to in the previous chapter).

It probably took about three million years for the London Clay to be laid down and over this period the sediment deposited on the sea floor slowly changed as did the types of animals that lived in the sea. Attempts have therefore been made to subdivide the London Clay into a number of zones based on the nature of the clay and the assemblage of fossils present. The classification mostly used nowadays is one devised by geologist Chris King which divides the formation into five divisions (A to E in ascending order) of which division E embraces the highest beds of the London Clay and also the sandy clay overlying it known as the Claygate Beds.

London Clay Fossils

The London Clay sea was home to turtles, sea-snakes, crocodiles and many species of fish including sharks, the largest of which was *Otodus obliquus* (fig. 33), an extinct ancestor of the great white shark. There was also the pearly nautilus, an animal with a spiral chambered shell, the descendants of which now live in the southern Pacific and Indian oceans. Other creatures include gastropods, bivalves, brachiopods, crinoids, crabs and lobsters. All these can be found as fossils in the London Clay although they are rather sparsely distributed.

The London Clay also contains one of the world's most varied fruit and seed floras with over 500 plant species recorded. Of the fruits and seeds found one of the most common is the fruit of the palm *Nipa*, a plant which survives today only in the mangrove swamps of south-east Asia. Study of these fossils has led to a comprehensive picture being put together of plant life during early Eocene times. Pieces of fossilized wood ranging in size from twigs to large logs are commonly found in the London Clay; they are usually riddled with holes (fig. 28) which were bored by the wood-boring bivalve *Teredina*, much like the present day ship worm *Teredo* which bores into wood floating in the sea. Fossilised wood, replaced by the mineral pyrite (see box), is often found washed out of the London Clay onto the foreshore around the Essex coast; at Walton-on-the-Naze, for example, parts of the beach are found to consist almost entirely of well preserved twigs and small fragments of fossilised wood. All the plant fossils found in the London Clay would have been brought down rivers in large floating masses of vegetation and carried out to sea.

In the middle of the nineteenth century the collection of cement stones for the Harwich cement industry led to important fossils being found, including many fine turtles (fig. 35). Of particular interest was the first discovery of *Coryphodon*, one of the largest Eocene plant-eating mammals, from a fragment of jaw, with teeth, dredged up off the coast. From subsequent fossils found in North America this creature appears to have been almost as large as a rhinoceros, having a large head and knife-like upper canine teeth. Also dredged up off the coast was a fragment of the Harwich Stone Band containing the skull and partial skeleton of the earliest horse *Hyracotherium*, also known as Eohippus (figs. 36 and 37). This tiny creature, no larger than a fox, had toes instead of hooves and its bones, like those of *Coryphodon*, must have drifted down a river on a raft of vegetation and been deposited on the floor of the London Clay sea. Many more fossil mammals from the London Clay have been found since those days, mostly from Walton, where collectors frequently search the beach for specimens. These fossils are of great importance as they provide us with an insight into the evolution of mammals following the extinction of the dinosaurs.

The London Clay also contains remarkably well preserved bones of birds, again mostly from Walton, a site which has produced a large number in recent years, mostly due to the efforts of local amateur collector Mike Daniels. In fact, the finds from Walton are the best preserved bird fauna of this age to be found anywhere in the world. The fossils are mostly from silty pockets in the lower part of the cliff (probably originally hollows on the ancient sea bed) which often contain associated bones of single individuals. The careful separation of the bones from the clay therefore allows the skeletons to be reconstructed. Some 150 species have been found including a parrot and a possible ancestor of the ostrich.

Treasures from the Clay

Minerals are natural elements or chemical compounds which are the constituents of all rocks. Some form beautiful crystals which are prized by collectors. Good specimens are rare in the relatively young, soft rocks of Essex but they do occasionally occur in the London Clay.

Pyrite (iron disulphide), also known as 'fools' gold', forms concretions in the clay and often occurs around pieces of fossil wood. From the seventeenth until the nineteenth century these pyrite nodules, or 'copperas stones' as they were called, were gathered from the Essex coast and used for making copperas (ferrous sulphate) for tanning (Chapter 9). Another mineral found is **barite** (barium sulphate), which sometimes forms attractive groups of crystals on green iron-bearing calcite that lines contraction cracks in the septarian nodules. Banded veins of green **calcite** (calcium carbonate), which is very attractive when cut and polished, are also found, particularly at Harwich and Wrabness.

Another mineral found in the London clay, usually within or just below the weathered zone of the clay, is **selenite**, a variety of **gypsum** (calcium sulphate), that forms clear crystals (fig. 39). Selenite results from the chemical reaction between sulphuric acid (formed from oxidising pyrite in the weathered zone) and the calcium carbonate of fossil shells.

Attractive mineral specimens from the London Clay can be found in museum collections throughout south-east England.

Exposures of London Clay in Essex

Although the London Clay is the most widespread geological formation in Essex, exposures are rare and the clay pits at High Ongar, South Ockendon and

Bulmer are the only visible excavations at present. High Ongar clay pit has, in the past, yielded some magnificent specimens, particularly the crab *Zanthopsis* (fig. 29) and various species of nautilus (fig. 32) but the quarry has now ceased working and is being infilled. South Ockendon clay pit (fig. 26) yielded teeth of a new species of sting ray and a number of bird bones in the mid-1970s. Gravel pits in the Chelmsford district occasionally reach the London Clay beneath the gravel but fossils from these localities are scarce. At Nag's Head Lane, near Warley, excavation of a deep cutting for the M25 motorway yielded a wealth of specimens to many collectors in 1981 making it the most famous temporary geological site in the county.

Much more accessible are the exposures of London Clay on the Essex coast where at many places, particularly along the estuaries of the Blackwater and Crouch, wide platforms of London Clay are revealed at low tide. At such places as Maylandsea and Steeple fine specimens of the lobster *Hoploparia* (fig. 30) can be collected from the wave-eroded surface of the clay, whilst at Osea Island stems of the crinoid or sea lily *Isselicrinus* (fig. 31) occur in abundance. Many of these sites were discovered as a result of a survey of the coast by amateur geologists Bill George and Stephen Vincent in the mid-1970s. One of the most prolific London Clay sites was at Althorne (fig. 38), where a cliff on an outer bend of the River Crouch is being eroded. Fossils are very difficult to find here nowadays but many crabs and thousands of sharks' teeth were collected from this locality in the early 1970s. Other coastal exposures are at Walton-on-the-Naze and Harwich. The beach at The Naze is currently the best site in Essex for collecting sharks' teeth and other London Clay fossils.

The Claygate Beds and the Bagshot Sand

Towards the top of the London Clay, seams of fine sand were laid down as the sea became shallower, this change marking the transition to the **Claygate Beds**; but the precise position of the junction is controversial. The Claygate Beds (also known as 'passage beds' because they form the transition between the London Clay and the Bagshot Sand) consist not only of sandy clays but also patches of stiff brown clay and fine-grained sand. Fossils are sometimes present, the bivalve *Venericardia trinobantium* (a cockle) being diagnostic of the Claygate Beds. The beds are found in central Essex, beneath isolated patches of Bagshot Sand, but there are very few permanent exposures.

As the sea became even shallower the Claygate Beds pass up into the almost unfossiliferous **Bagshot Sand**. This delightful pale yellow to orange brown fine-grained sand caps the high ground in central and southern Essex as, for example, at High Beach, Havering-atte-Bower, Brentwood, Kelvedon Hatch, Billericay, Danbury, Rayleigh and the Langdon Hills (fig. 83). These are isolated remnants of a continuous deposit up to 25 metres (80 feet) thick that must have covered the whole of Essex but has been largely removed by erosion.

At the very top of the Bagshot Sand at some places is a layer of pebbles called the **Bagshot Pebble Bed**, a beach gravel formed as the shoreline passed finally over Essex. These well-rounded flint pebbles can be seen in the fields around the village of Stock, south of Chelmsford. Unfortunately there are now no significant exposures of the Bagshot Sand in Essex; the last known exposure - a disused brick pit on Hambro Hill, near Rayleigh - was filled in during the summer of 1990. Small patches of Bagshot Sand are, however, visible on the steeply sloping ground to the north-west of The Kings Oak Inn at High Beach in Epping Forest.

In this story of the geological history of Essex we are dealing with progressively younger rocks and modern species of animals and plants slowly appear in the fossil record. It has been estimated that about 3 per cent of species living in the Eocene Epoch still exist today.

Any sediments that may have been laid down in the 45 million years or so following deposition of the Bagshot Sand no longer occur in Essex because of erosion, much of which probably took place during the Miocene Epoch when the area was land. During Miocene times (about 20 million years ago) the strong movements of the Earth's crust that created the Alps also tilted and compressed south-east England, creating the London Basin. The next period represented by surviving sediments is the Pliocene.

Fig. 26 London Clay being excavated at South Ockendon. *(Photo: G. Lucy)*

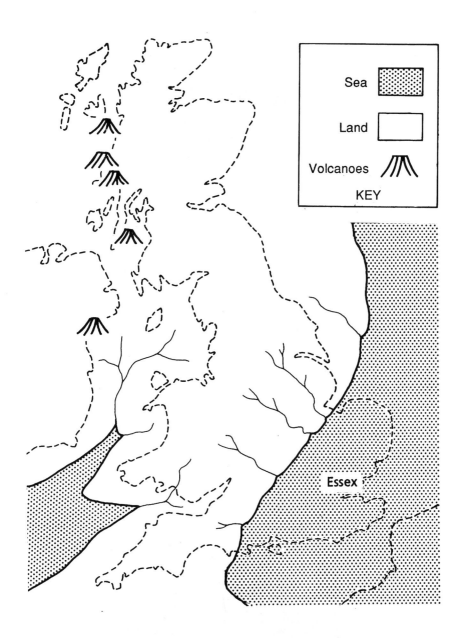

Fig. 27 A possible geography of Britain during Lower Eocene times (approximately 55 million years ago). The climate was subtropical and the coastline thickly forested. Rivers brought mud and silt into the shallow sea that covered south-east England forming, over a three million year period, the familiar London Clay that underlies most of Essex. The map shows the maximum likely area of sea; the coastline was much closer to Essex for most of this period.

Fig. 28 Fossilised wood riddled with the borings of the bivalve *Teredina* from the London Clay at High Ongar. This 'ship worm' attacked logs of wood floating in the subtropical sea.

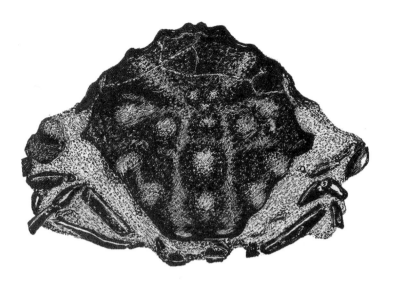

Fig. 29 The crab *Zanthopsis leachi* from the London Clay at High Ongar. Fossil crabs from the former clay pit at High Ongar were remarkably well preserved.

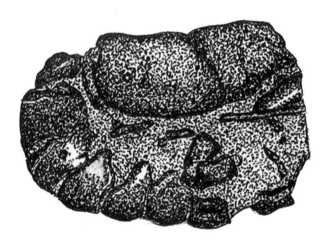

Fig. 30 The lobster *Hoploparia gammaroides* from the London Clay at Steeple, near Maldon. The carapace (the outer shell) and the tail are well preserved in this specimen.

Fig. 31 Part of the stem of the crinoid *Isselicrinus subbasaltiformis* from the London Clay at Aveley.

Fig. 32 The preserved centre of the pearly nautilus *Simplicioceras centrale* from the London Clay at High Ongar. Complete specimens are usually distorted or crushed.

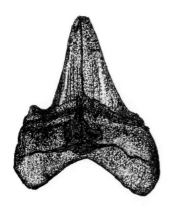

Fig. 33 Tooth of the large shark *Otodus obliquus* from the London Clay at Althorne, near Burnham-on-Crouch.

Fig. 34 Tooth of the shark *Eugomphodus macrotus* from the London Clay at South Ockendon. One of the commonest of the sharks' teeth found in the London Clay.

Fig. 35 A magnificent specimen of the turtle *Neurochelys harvicensis* from the London Clay of Harwich. Preserved in a septarian nodule, it is 50 centimetres (20 inches) in length and is currently on display at the Castle Museum, Norwich. It is one of many fossil turtles collected by workmen employed in the Harwich cement industry in the early nineteenth century.
(Illustration: The Palaeontographical Society)

50

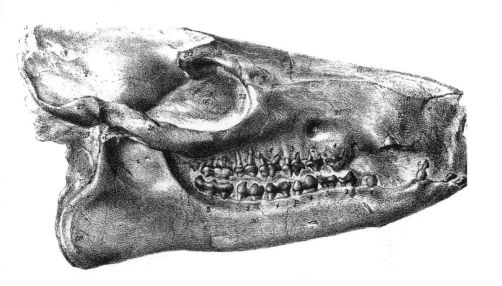

Fig. 36 The skull of *Hyracotherium* (formerly known as *Eohippus*), an early ancestor of the horse, found in the nineteenth century in the London Clay at Harwich. This creature was no larger than a fox and must have lived on riverside vegetation, its body being carried by a river into the London Clay sea. *(Illustration from the Proceedings of the Geological Society)*

Fig. 37 An artist's impression of *Hyracotherium*. *(By courtesy of the Natural History Museum)*

Fig. 38 Collecting fossils from the foreshore at Althorne on the River Crouch. In the background is a low cliff of London Clay. *(Photo: G. Lucy)*

Fig. 39 Crystals of selenite (a variety of the mineral gypsum) from the London Clay, found during excavations for the M25 motorway at Brentwood. The specimen on the left is 10 centimetres (4 inches) in length. *(Photo: G. Lucy)*

Chapter 7

GIANT SHARKS AND SHELL BANKS

The Red Crag Sea

About 3 million years ago, at the very end of the Pliocene Epoch, most of Essex was slowly covered by a sea between 15 and 25 metres (50 to 80 feet) deep and the climate was relatively cool. As the sea advanced across Essex a shelly sand containing an abundance of marine shells was laid down as dunes on the sea bed, fairly close to the shoreline. This now forms a deposit called the **Red Crag** which underlies much of north Essex and Suffolk. The word 'crag' was formerly a local term used in East Anglia to describe fine gravel and sand but geologists have now adopted it to designate some of the characteristic marine deposits of Pliocene and Pleistocene age in Essex, Suffolk and Norfolk.

Red Crag in Essex

The most spectacular exposure of Red Crag in East Anglia is at Walton-on-the-Naze where, in the cliffs to the north of the town, the red, shelly sand can be seen resting on the blue-grey London Clay. Walton is one of the finest geological sites in Britain; both the Red Crag and the London Clay here are of international importance and the cliffs are designated a Site of Special Scientific Interest.

The rust-red colour of the sand and its contained fossils is the most distinctive feature of the cliffs and is due to the former presence of pyrite which was washed from the London Clay into the Red Crag and there oxidised. The final product of this chemical reaction is a red iron oxide which has stained the shell debris producing the attractive colours. Although the geology of the Naze is straightforward with one formation lying on top of another, this has been complicated by extensive landslips. Rain water seeping through the sands runs out on meeting the impervious clay, with the result that slumped masses of shelly sand are continually sliding down to be removed rapidly by waves lapping against the foot of the cliff (fig. 42). As a result the Naze is also an excellent example of coastal erosion.

The Red Crag at Walton displays **sedimentary structures** which are evidence of the conditions that existed on the sea bed at the time of deposition. Of these, **cross bedding** is the most common, where the movement of sand 'dunes' by undersea currents has formed inclined layers; from this evidence it is possible to establish current strength and direction. Also visible in the cliffs are small vertical cylinders of cemented sand which were formerly the burrows of marine animals; they are known as **trace fossils** and are also present in other formations such as the Woolwich Beds (fig. 20). Many people have worked on the Walton Crag. The most famous was probably Norfolk amateur geologist F.W. Harmer whose research findings, from work carried out around the turn of the century, is still accepted today.

In Essex, Red Crag was formerly thought to exist only in the Walton area and in other isolated patches in the north-east of the county; but surveys carried out by the British Geological Survey in the 1980s revealed that it extended west as far as Stansted Mountfitchet (fig. 3), although there it is mostly buried beneath drift deposits. In the west of Essex it had not been previously recognised because in most cases it has been decalcified, i.e. all the fossil shells have been dissolved by percolating ground waters. It is sometimes exposed in gravel pits such as at Canfield, Elsenham, Halstead, Stebbing and Widdington. There was formerly an exposure of shelly Red Crag on the coast at Harwich but this was entirely destroyed by the action of the sea in the nineteenth century. It was, however, recorded by Samuel Dale in 1730 in his book *The History and Antiquities of Harwich and Dovercourt* (fig. 45) which was the first book to describe and illustrate fossils from Essex.

The base of the Red Crag is only about 15 metres (50 feet) above present sea level at Walton but further west it is much higher, reaching 90 metres (300 feet) at Elsenham. This is due to a rise of the land during the Ice Age coupled with a subsidence of the North Sea floor.

Red Crag Fossils

The Red Crag at Walton is highly fossiliferous and some layers appear to consist almost entirely of fossil shells. The fauna is diverse and well preserved and hundreds of species have been recorded. Corals, echinoids and barnacles can be found but by far the most common fossils are bivalves and gastropods such as the dog cockle *Glycymeris glycymeris* (fig. 43) and the 'left handed' whelk *Neptunea contraria* (fig. 44). The latter is so called because it spirals the 'wrong way', in other words in the opposite direction to almost every other gastropod. In addition, sharks' teeth can be found, most being derived from the underlying London Clay but some are from Miocene and Red Crag sharks. It has been estimated that about half of the fossils in the Red Crag are of species that are still living today.

Between the Red Crag and the London Clay, there is, in some places, a thin layer of phosphatic nodules and fossils derived from the London Clay. In this layer there are also well-rounded lumps of very hard sandstone called 'boxstones' believed to be of Miocene age. If these rather uninteresting-looking lumps are Miocene they are the only rocks of this age in Britain; the Miocene is the only gap in Britain's otherwise remarkably complete geological record. This basal nodule bed was formerly worked as a source of phosphate fertiliser at Wrabness and at Walton. The nodule bed also yields very rolled and highly polished bones of whale and large terrestrial mammals such as ancestors of the elephant; together with the fossil teeth of the giant shark *Carcharodon megalodon* (see box). These fossils were washed into the Red Crag sea from rocks of Miocene age which were removed by marine erosion long ago, and possibly recycled several times before being incorporated in the Red Crag. No doubt the more durable fossils from the nodule bed will become incorporated into sediments now being laid down on the floor of the North Sea, along with present day shells and human artifacts, to be exhumed sometime in the distant future. At Walton, digging in the cliffs is not permitted but fossils from the nodule bed can be readily found on the beach.

Little work appears to have been done on the mammal and shark fossils from the nodule bed despite the remarkable collection of specimens in Ipswich Museum from the Suffolk Red Crag sites. The remarkably high polish shown by the fossil bones and teeth is still a mystery. Their well-rounded appearance indicates rolling in water with a high current velocity, but it is difficult to see how this movement could also have polished them to the degree we now see.

Fig. 40 A close up of the cliffs at Walton-on-the-Naze showing Red Crag sand crowded with fossil shells. A cross section through sea floor sediments over two million years old. *(Photo: G. Lucy)*

Fig. 41 An aerial view of the cliffs at Walton-on-the-Naze. The photograph was taken in 1977. *(Photo : Cambridge University Collection. Copyright reserved.)*

56

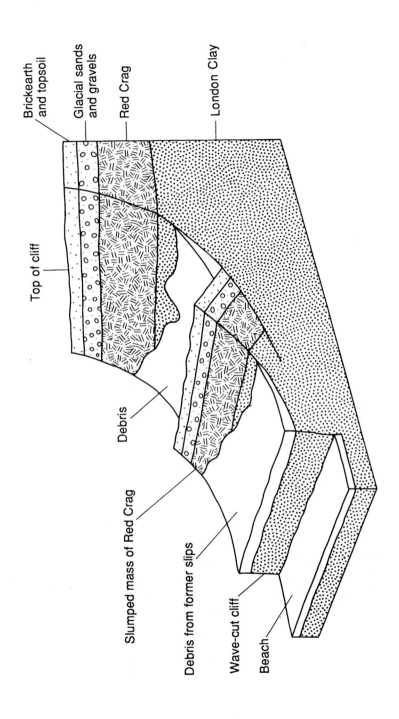

Brickearth
and topsoil

Glacial sands
and gravels

Red Crag

London Clay

Top of cliff

Debris

Slumped mass of Red Crag

Debris from former slips

Wave-cut cliff

Beach

Fig. 42 Typical cross-section through the cliff at The Naze, Walton, showing a landslip.

57

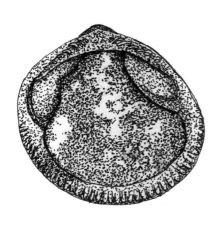

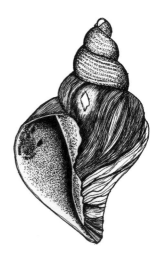

Fig. 43 The bivalve *Glycymeris glycymeris* from the Red Crag at Walton-on-the-Naze. This cockle still lives on the British coast today.

Fig. 44 The 'left-handed' whelk *Neptunia contraria* from the Red Crag at Walton-on-the-Naze. The most popular Red Crag fossil.

Tab. VIII. *Page 44.*

A.Land-guard-Fort.B. *The Andrews or Barr of Sand runing from the Fort.* C.*The South or Dover Court Point of the Havens mouth.* DD.*The Strata of* Sand, Gravel, Foſſil-Shells, *and their Fragments.* E.*The Stratum of* Blewiſh Clay *diver⸗ Feet deep.* F.*The heep of Gravel,* Sand, & Shells.&c.*which caving down from the Top ly at the bottom of the Cliff.* G.Cliff-Stones. *which ly upon the Shore before the Cliff.* H.*Perſons Obſerving The Cliff.* I.A Stone *of the Lower or Stoney Stratum.*

R.Sheard

Fig. 45 A cliff of Red Crag that formerly existed at Harwich. From *The History and Antiquities of Harwich and Dovercourt* by Samuel Dale, published in 1730. *(Reproduced by courtesy of the Essex Record Office)*

58

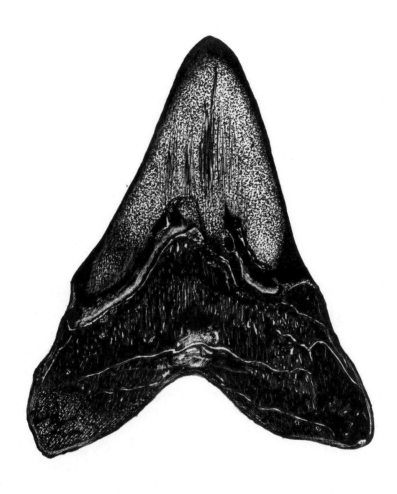

Fig. 46 Tooth of the giant shark *Carcharodon megalodon* **(10 centimetres (4 inches) in length) from the Red Crag at Walton-on-the-Naze.** This is the largest shark known, probably reaching a length of 12 metres (40 feet).

Fossil Sharks

Many of the rocks of Essex contain large numbers of sharks' teeth. Could this be evidence that prehistoric seas were once teeming with sharks?

Teeth are usually the only part of a shark to be fossilised because the skeleton contains no bone and is entirely composed of cartilage, an elastic substance that is found in most vertebrates. This is one of the features that distinguishes sharks from all other fish. Another feature is the arrangement of teeth which exist in rows with only the front row in use at any one time. The teeth are only loosely attached to the jaws and are often torn away allowing fresh teeth to move forward to take their place. This rapid turnover of teeth is thought to account for the vast numbers that accumulate on the sea floor to be preserved as fossils.

The largest of all sharks was the awesome *Carcharodon megalodon* whose fossil teeth can exceed 10 centimetres (4 inches) in length (fig. 46). This animal is thought to have been over 12 metres (40 feet) long with gaping jaws that may have been large enough to accommodate a standing man. The teeth of this extinct shark are rare but they can occasionally be found on the beach at Walton, derived from the Red Crag.

Global Cooling

The fossil molluscs in the Red Crag are of cold climate species and pollen grains indicate that the nearby coastline was dominated by pine forest; an indication of climatic deterioration. The British Isles was beginning to feel the effects of the coming Ice Age. The world was entering the coldest stage of a gradual cooling that had commenced some 30 million years before. This ice age was to become the fourth ice age to have occurred on Earth in the last 1,000 million years.

Chapter 8

THE ICE AGE

The Onset of the Ice Age

For most of geological time, the Earth's surface has been warm and free of ice but periodically, for reasons we do not fully understand, global temperatures drop and the world experiences an ice age. Geologists have not found it easy to reach agreement on the position of the geological boundary that marks the beginning of the present Ice Age (the start of the Quaternary Era) but it is currently considered to be approximately 1.6 million years ago.

An ice age is a time when ice is present at the poles and on mountain ranges. During an ice age there are cold periods when the ice flows out from these regions as gigantic ice sheets extending hundreds of kilometres onto the lowlands to form continuous ice fronts thousands of kilometres long. These cold periods are interspersed with temperate periods when the ice sheets retreat and the climate can even be warmer than the present day with animals such as elephant and hippopotamus living in southern England.

Evidence for these fluctuations in global temperature has been preserved in the clays, sands and gravels of Essex giving us some idea of the changing climate over the last million years or so. Unfortunately, the picture of the earlier part of the present Ice Age is less clear because so much has been obliterated by subsequent glacial and river erosion. However, one early Ice Age deposit that has survived in Essex is the **Norwich Crag**.

The Norwich Crag Sea

Beneath much of north Essex and lying directly on the Red Crag is a layer of sand mostly 5-10 metres (15-30 feet) thick which forms part of the Norwich Crag formation. This deposit, called the **Chillesford Sand**, was probably laid down in an estuary about one and a half million years ago. The exact age of the Norwich Crag is controversial and some researchers regard it as Pliocene.

The Chillesford Sand is comprised of a medium-grained sand varying in colour from yellow and orange to grey and occasionally containing seams of flint pebbles. Although fossils occur in the Chillesford Sand in Suffolk, none have been found in this deposit in Essex. There are, however, numerous sedimentary structures, particularly cross bedding, which provide evidence of tidal currents. The Norwich Crag is so called because the deposit extends beneath Norwich in Norfolk.

Period	Age in years	Stage	Climate in Essex	Geology in Essex	Archaeology
Holocene	0	Flandrian	Warming	Alluvium, peat beds and recent coastal deposits	Neolithic
	5 000		Deterioration		
			Warmest period of Flandrian (Britain becomes an island)		Mesolithic
	10 000		Warming (rise in sea levels)		
Pleistocene	20 000	Devensian	Glacial	Terrace deposits in the Lea valley and at Great Totham	Palaeolithic
	100 000				
	125 000	Ipswichian	Temperate	'Hippo gravels' at East Mersea	
	200 000	Wolstonian	Glacial / interglacial sequence	Deposits at Ilford and Aveley	
	400 000	Hoxnian	Temperate	Marks Tey lake deposits Clacton channel deposits Low Level East Essex Gravel	First evidence of man in Essex (Clacton)
	450 000	Anglian	Glacial	Boulder clay and glacial gravel	
	500 000	Early Pleistocene stages	Climate of early stages uncertain	High Level East Essex Gravel Kesgrave Sands and Gravels	First evidence of man in Britain (Sussex)
				High level gravels capping hills in central Essex	
	1.6 million			Norwich Crag	
Pliocene				Red Crag	

Fig. 47 Time scale of the Ice Age (not to scale). We are currently living in the Flandrian interglacial stage.

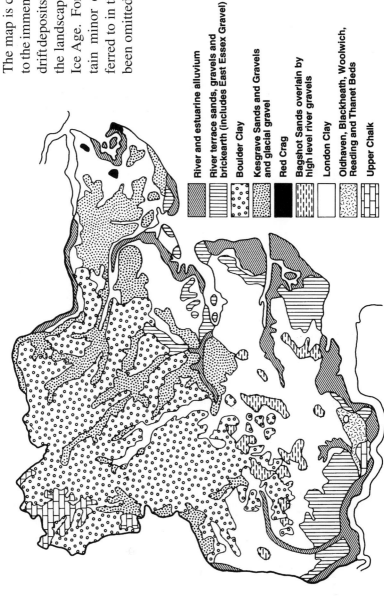

Fig. 48 Geological map of Essex (solid and drift).

The map is complex due to the immense variety of drift deposits that covered the landscape during the Ice Age. For clarity certain minor deposits referred to in the text have been omitted.

River and estuarine alluvium

River terrace sands, gravels and brickearth (includes East Essex Gravel)

Boulder Clay

Kesgrave Sands and Gravels and glacial gravel

Red Crag

Bagshot Sands overlain by high level river gravels

London Clay

Oldhaven, Blackheath, Woolwich, Reading and Thanet Beds

Upper Chalk

63

A History of the River Thames

In the early years of this century it was suggested that the Thames might not always have followed its present course but may have originally flowed to the north of London, across north Essex and into Suffolk. It was not until the 1970s that research finally confirmed that the sands and gravels which lie directly on the Chillesford Sand and underlie large areas of north and central Essex (and are known as the **Kesgrave Sands and Gravels**) were actually deposited by this early Thames. It is now known that the Thames even reached as far as Norfolk and its course slowly migrated south over hundreds of thousands of years until, about 500,000 years ago, it was a huge braided river flowing across a wide flood plain between Harlow and Colchester. The Kesgrave Sands and Gravels are worked extensively in many gravel pits in the Chelmsford, Braintree and Colchester areas and contain many pebbles, known as **exotics**, that have travelled a considerable distance. Some are of volcanic rocks from North Wales, which has led to the theory that the upper Severn drainage basin was once part of the headwaters of the Thames.

Research has also shown that for much of this time the River Medway flowed north across east Essex to join the Thames north of Clacton; evidence for this is in the form of gravels found between Rayleigh and Bradwell-on-Sea which contain a mixture of rocks from Kent. They are collectively known as **High Level East Essex Gravel** and include the patches of gravel on top of the Rayleigh Hills. Fig. 49 shows probable early courses of the Thames and Medway rivers.

'High level' gravels associated with other rivers that flowed across Essex can be found resting on the Bagshot Sand and capping the areas of high ground in central Essex as at High Beach, Brentwood, Billericay, Danbury and the Langdon Hills (fig. 83), but the dating of these deposits (formerly called Pebble Gravel) has proved to be extremely difficult. It is thought that these gravels were laid down by rivers flowing north into the early Thames. At Warley, near Brentwood, these gravels (known locally as Warley Gravel) contain a large number of cigar-shaped pebbles which are mostly found with their longer axes vertical. This curious phenomenon has been attributed to repeated freezing and thawing of the ground during subsequent cold periods. Some of these isolated patches of gravel are found at elevations of over 100 metres (300 feet) above present day sea level; it is therefore difficult to imagine that each of these hilltops was once the floor of an ancient river valley. It has been suggested, however, that the hills may owe their existence to the river gravel which slowed down erosion while the higher land surrounding the valleys was reduced to the present lowland. Interestingly, it has been said that the name High Beach may be derived from an early English description of the sand and gravel exposures in this part of Epping Forest.

About 450,000 years ago a great ice sheet (known as the Anglian ice sheet) spread south into Essex blocking the Thames valley upstream and diverting the river to roughly its present course (see box). When the river reached Southend it then flowed north as a combined Thames/Medway river along the old Medway valley towards Clacton. Evidence for this combined river is the **Low Level East Essex Gravel** which contains not only the characteristic rocks from Kent but now also a significant proportion of rocks from the west, brought in by the Thames. At this time, when sea level was much lower and Britain was joined to the continent, the river flowed out from Clacton across the low-lying land that is now the southern North Sea to become a tributary of the Rhine.

The Diversion of the Thames

Geologists have known for some time that about 450,000 years ago a catastrophic change affected the Thames causing it to alter its course and adopt the route we know today. But just how rapid this change was has only recently been appreciated by examining the sands and gravels at two sites in north-east Essex.

The study of gravels in a quarry at St. Osyth and in the cliffs at Holland-on-Sea by David Bridgland and others has revealed when and just how suddenly the Thames ceased to flow through central Essex as a result of being blocked upstream in Hertfordshire by a lobe of ice from the Anglian ice sheet. Also, clays and silts discovered in what is now the Vale of St. Albans provide evidence of a great lake filled by the Thames until it finally spilled over to take the now familiar route to the sea.

This picture has been built up by painstaking detective work comparing not only the structure of the various deposits (indicating current strength and direction) but more importantly their composition (the distribution of rock types) from which it has been possible to establish with some accuracy the route of this ancient river.

In north-east Essex there are many important sites which provide evidence of the evolution of the Thames/Medway river system. In particular, sites at Ardleigh, Clacton, East Mersea, Little Oakley, St. Osyth and Wivenhoe have given us a picture of the geography of the area during this middle part of the Ice Age. Some of these sites have yielded fossils such as at Cudmore Grove, East Mersea (fig. 82) where there is a 'channel deposit' associated with the post-diversion Thames/Medway river which has yielded bones of beaver, bear and monkey. In the cliffs at Clacton there is another channel deposit equivalent in age to that at East Mersea and a downstream continuation of the Thames/Medway. This famous site (now obscured by sea defences) was discovered in the 1830s by Essex amateur geologist John Brown, and has produced not only the bones of lion, rhinoceros and straight-tusked elephant (fig. 65), but also flint tools (fig. 66) representing the earliest evidence of man's presence in Essex. Most exposures of these gravels, however, contain no fossils and geologists have been relying on more ingenious methods of dating them. One of these methods involves the study, at Ardleigh and Wivenhoe, of a red clay layer in the gravel which is thought to be an ancient soil horizon (the Valley Farm Soil) formed during a warm period; the degree of reddening indicating the temperature under which it was formed. Another layer on top of this (the Barham Soil) indicates soil formation under intensely cold conditions. This research should eventually lead to the correlation of these Thames deposits with the early Ice Age sequences elsewhere in Britain and on the Continent.

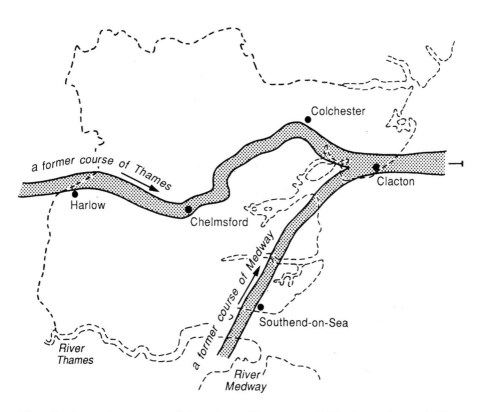

Fig. 49 An early course of the rivers Thames and Medway through Essex (approximately 500,000 years ago) prior to the arrival of the Anglian ice sheet. The existence of pebbles from Kent in the High Level East Essex Gravel is evidence that the River Medway originally flowed through Essex to join this early course of the Thames. *(After Bridgland 1994)*

Glaciers and Ice Sheets

As world temperatures fluctuated between cold and warm periods over hundreds of thousands of years the ice sheets periodically advanced and retreated. The period of maximum advance of the ice sheets is known as a glacial stage or **glaciation** and that of maximum retreat as an interglacial stage or **interglacial**. During glaciations so much water was locked up in ice sheets that sea level fell to very low levels, in some cases as low as 120 metres (400 feet) lower than today.

In Britain the greatest glaciation is called the **Anglian** and occurred about 450,000 years ago. During this time an ice sheet up to one kilometre (over half a mile) thick reached as far south as Hornchurch (fig. 51). The railway cutting at Hornchurch, which first exposed Anglian glacial deposits when it was excavated in 1892, is therefore one of the most important Pleistocene sites in Britain, providing evidence of the southern-most limit of the ice during the whole of the Ice Age. The Anglian ice sheet was responsible for diverting the Thames to its present course. During glaciations the average temperature in Britain could have been as low as minus 9°C.

In Britain, in addition to the Anglian, there is evidence of at least two other major glaciations but there were also many minor advances of the ice sheet during these and also during each interglacial. There is also evidence of at least two major interglacial periods - the **Hoxnian** and the **Ipswichian** (fig. 47). During these intervals the average annual temperature was higher than it is today.

During the most recent glaciation, the **Devensian**, the ice sheet extended only as far south as Norfolk (fig. 74) but the extremely cold temperatures throughout Essex at this time have left their mark on the landscape. These **periglacial** features include **ice wedge polygons** which are formed when the ground shrinks and cracks creating a network of ice wedges. Each summer, the cracks filled with water which later froze widening the cracks; a process which continued throughout the glacial stage. At the end of the Devensian glaciation, 10,000 years ago, these cracks filled with debris preserving them as **ice wedge casts** which are sometimes revealed as **crop marks** in fields of crops during hot, dry summers (fig. 62). Much older ice wedge casts (from the early part of the Anglian glacial stage) are sometimes preserved in the Kesgrave Sands and Gravels beneath boulder clay and revealed by quarrying (fig. 63).

During these cold periods the ground was permanently frozen (and known as **permafrost**) with only the top layer of soil thawing during each brief summer. When thawed this 'active layer' was saturated with water and was capable of slowly flowing down a slope. This slow process, known as **solifluction**, has produced a reworked deposit called **head**, the nature of which depends on the rocks involved. In Essex it is commonly found both on hillsides and in valley bottoms.

Residues that remained after the ice had melted, and also material distributed by rivers flowing off a melting ice sheet, are called **glacial drift**. Boulder clay and glacial gravel are examples of glacial drift.

Boulder Clay

As the ice moved it ground up and carried along pieces of the rocks over which it passed, just as glaciers and ice sheets do today. When the ice melted an unsorted clayey residue called **boulder clay** or **till** was left behind (fig. 54). This contains boulders transported long distances by the ice and deposited in areas remote from their sources. Such boulders are called **glacial erratics** (see box). The Anglian ice sheet extended into Essex as far south as Chigwell, Hornchurch and Hanningfield, so that the area to the north of this line is covered by boulder clay except where it has been subsequently removed by erosion. The boulder clay is mostly between 10 and 15 metres (30 to 50 feet) thick but in some places in the north of the county it can reach a thickness of over 40 metres (130 feet).

The composition of boulder clay varies according to the rocks over which the ice passed. In Essex it contains much chalk (when it is, not surprisingly, known as **chalky boulder clay**) and in the north-west of the county near Widdington it can almost resemble chalk in appearance. The lower part is often dark grey as it contains ground up Jurassic rocks from much further north. Boulder clay can be seen in the gravel pits around Chelmsford and Braintree and it is commonly encountered in temporary excavations in the north of the county. Many fossils (figs. 57-60) can be found in the boulder clay but they have often been broken and abraded by transport within the ice. A large number of these fossils are of Jurassic age, such as ammonites and belemnites; all of them brought to Essex from the Midlands.

Some boulders from the boulder clay are large; a septarian nodule 2 metres (6 feet) in diameter, also brought here from Jurassic rocks in the Midlands, is permanently on display in the grounds of Saffron Walden Museum. One feature characteristic of glacially transported boulders is the presence of scratches or striations which were received when the rocks passed over each other either within or at the base of the ice sheet (fig. 55). Boulder clay in Essex also contains igneous rocks which have been transported from as far away as Scotland and Scandinavia.

Most of the lower, dark grey boulder clay in Essex is thought to be **lodgement till**, which was deposited as debris 'lodged' at the base of the moving ice sheet. Any long, thin pebbles within this boulder clay will therefore be aligned with their long axes parallel to the direction of ice flow. By carefully excavating around these pebbles and measuring their compass orientation the local direction of ice movement across Essex can be established.

The boulder clay in Essex has, in the past, been called the Lowestoft Till.

Some deposits of boulder clay in certain parts of Essex have also been given local names (e.g. the Springfield Till and Hanningfield Till), and some geologists have attributed these to different advances of the Anglian ice sheet.

Imported Rocks

The boulder clay of Essex contains many glacial erratics that have been transported from distant locations. An amazing variety of rocks can be found and by matching rock types with known outcrops in other parts of Britain geologists are able to establish the direction of ice movement across the country from its origins in Scotland or Scandinavia.

Some of the largest glacial erratics found in Essex can be seen in prominent positions in villages and towns. Most of these are puddingstones and sarsens (chapter 5) but other rock types are sometimes encountered. A comprehensive survey of these Essex stones was undertaken by A.E. Salter who published a list of those he found in The Essex Naturalist (the journal of The Essex Field Club) in 1914. Road widening has swept some of the stones away but many of them have survived. There is a need for an updated survey so that highway and planning authorities can be informed of their importance.

The vast majority of the boulders and pebbles in the Kesgrave Sands and Gravels were brought to Essex from the west by the early River Thames. Almost all are flint (some containing fossils from the Chalk sea) but there is also quartzite and puddingstone. Various pebbles of quartz and volcanic rocks derived from North Wales are also present and this indicates that the Thames may have originally drained the Welsh mountains before its headwaters were captured by the River Severn. Large pieces of silicified fossil wood (wood replaced by quartz) may also be found in these gravels and these can sometimes reveal beautiful colour banding and growth rings when cut and polished. The source of this fossil wood, and thus its age, has never been established.

Occasionally a specimen is found which creates a lot of interest. One such pebble, collected in 1987 from the Kesgrave Sands and Gravels at a Chelmsford gravel quarry was, because of its tin content and unique composition, proved to have originated in Cornwall. Its 400 million year journey had been via many ancient river systems before it was finally brought to Essex from the Midlands by the ancestral Thames.

Glacial Sand and Gravel

Meltwater running from the Anglian ice sheet washed away the finer fractions of the boulder clay and redeposited the coarser constituents as **glacial sand and gravel**, whilst the very fine material settled in lakes to form **glacial lake deposits** which consist of laminated silts and clay. Lack of sorting of the constituents are typical features of such rapidly deposited gravels. In Essex, glacial sand and gravel sometimes occurs under boulder clay and may have been formed in front of an advancing ice sheet.

Many deposits of sand and gravel that are marked on geological maps as glacial in origin are now known to be Kesgrave Sands and Gravels deposited by the Thames when it flowed far to the north of its present course.

Buried Valleys

In parts of East Anglia boreholes have revealed deep, steep-sided valleys cut into the chalk bedrock and now completely filled with glacial drift and hidden by a covering of boulder clay. Known as buried tunnel valleys or buried channels these remarkable natural features were formed beneath the Anglian ice sheet and were the main drainage routes for meltwater. To carve such deep channels the gravel-laden water must have been under tremendous pressure (due to the weight of the ice above) and the irregular surface of the channel floors indicate that in some places the water was even forced uphill.

In Essex, the best example of a buried channel is the Cam-Stort Buried Channel which is present from Great Chesterford near the Cambridgeshire border south as far as Bishop's Stortford. It passes beneath the village of Newport where it is more than 100 metres (300 feet) deep; almost half of this depth being below present sea level.

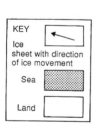

Fig. 50 The maximum extent of the ice sheet during the Anglian glaciation (approximately 450,000 years ago).

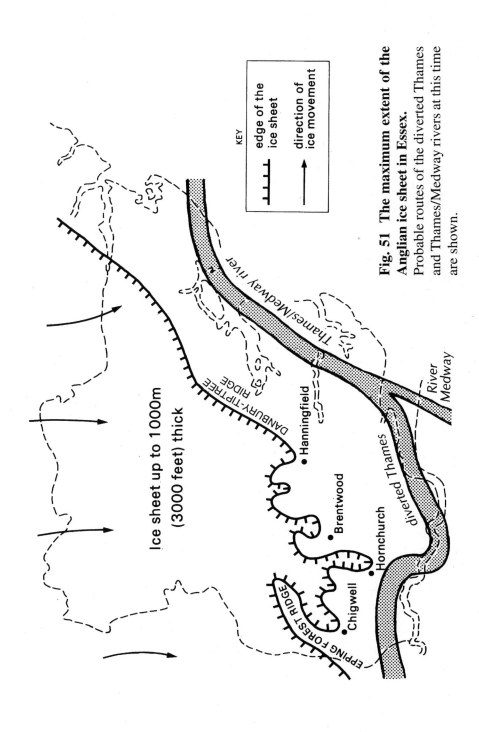

KEY

⊢⊢⊢⊢ edge of the ice sheet

→ direction of ice movement

Fig. 51 The maximum extent of the Anglian ice sheet in Essex. Probable routes of the diverted Thames and Thames/Medway rivers at this time are shown.

Ice sheet up to 1000m (3000 feet) thick

DANBURY-TIPTREE RIDGE

Thames/Medway river

River Medway

diverted Thames

• Hanningfield

Brentwood

Hornchurch

Chigwell

EPPING FOREST RIDGE

71

Fig. 52 Kesgrave Sands and Gravels overlain by boulder clay at a gravel quarry near Braintree. The sands and gravels were deposited by the Thames when it flowed across central Essex and the boulder clay was subsequently spread over the area by the Anglian ice sheet. *(Photo: G. Lucy)*

Fig. 53 An aerial view of the edge of the present day Greenland ice sheet.
A view of Chelmsford from the air about 450,000 years ago would have been very
similar as the Anglian ice sheet reached its maximum extent.
(Photo: Times Newspapers Ltd.)

Fig. 54 Residue from an ice sheet. Chalky boulder clay from north Essex. The large pebble of chalk is 7 centimetres (3 inches) long. *(Photo: G. Lucy)*

Fig. 55 A fragment of a septarian nodule showing scratches received at the base of the moving ice sheet. This specimen is from the Oxford Clay of the Midlands and was found in boulder clay near Braintree. *(Photo: G. Lucy)*

Fig. 56 A large septarian nodule from the Oxford Clay of the Midlands.
This nodule was found in boulder clay at a gravel quarry near Chelmsford in 1992.
It was broken in two by the excavator, revealing the characteristic internal cracks
lined with attractive calcite crystals. The surface of the nodule was found to be
decorated with fossil ammonites. *(Photo: G. Lucy)*

Fig. 57 The Jurassic ammonite *Amoeboceras serratum* from boulder clay near Braintree.

This specimen was brought to Essex from the Ampthill Clay of the Midlands and is about 160 million years old. Ammonites are extinct relatives of the present day nautilus and were extremely common in the seas during the Jurassic Period. Note the complex suture lines which mark the divisions between the chambers of the ammonite shell.

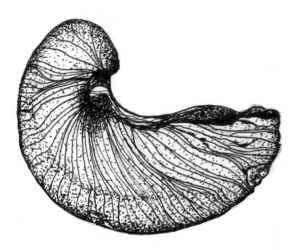

Fig. 58 The Jurassic bivalve *Gryphaea arcuata* (also known as the 'devil's toenail') from boulder clay near Chelmsford. It is from the Lower Lias clay of the Midlands and about 190 million years old. Fossils such as this often turn up in ploughed fields and gardens on the boulder clay plateau of north Essex.

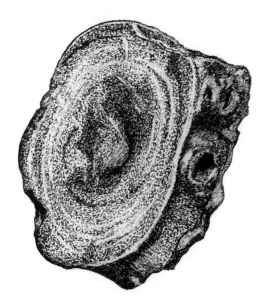

Fig. 59 Vertebra (part of the backbone) of a Jurassic ichthyosaur from boulder clay at High Ongar. Probably from the Oxford Clay of the Midlands and about 160 million years old. Ichthyosaurs were fast-swimming predators common in the seas during the time of the dinosaurs.

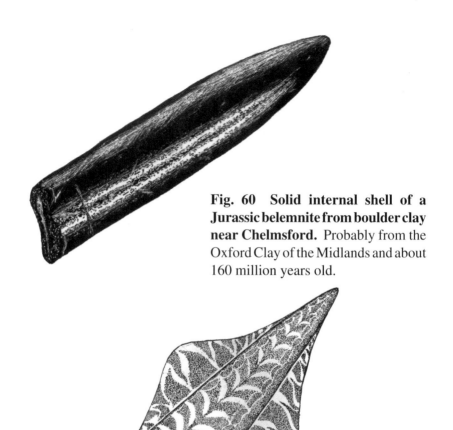

Fig. 60 Solid internal shell of a Jurassic belemnite from boulder clay near Chelmsford. Probably from the Oxford Clay of the Midlands and about 160 million years old.

Fig. 61 A reconstruction of a belemnite during life. Belemnites are extinct molluscs related to the squid and cuttlefish and were extremely common in the seas during the Jurassic Period.

Fig. 62 A strongly developed pattern of ice wedge polygons revealed by crop marks in fields near Whalebone Lane, Romford. The photograph was taken during the dry summer of 1976 when the crop marks were well displayed. *(Photo : Cambridge University Collection. Copyright reserved)*

Fig. 63   A section through a fossil ice wedge in gravels at Stanway, near Colchester. The scale is given by the geological hammer.
(By permission of the Director, British Geological Survey. Copyright NERC)

Fig. 64 A magnificent flint hand-axe found in 1981 in excavations for the M25 motorway at Belhus Park, Aveley. The axe is 22 centimetres (9 inches) long (old style 50p coin for scale) and photographed as found. It is in gravels of a middle terrace of the Thames and approximately 280,000 years old. *(Photo: G.R. Ward)*

Fig. 65 Two views of a straight-tusked elephant tooth found at Clacton in the nineteenth century. The original owner of this tooth was living during the Hoxnian interglacial stage (approximately 400,000 years ago) on the banks of the Thames/Medway river. Despite its name, this elephant does have curved tusks but they are curved in one plane, unlike the mammoth whose tusks are curved in three dimensions. *(Illustration: The Palaeontographical Society)*

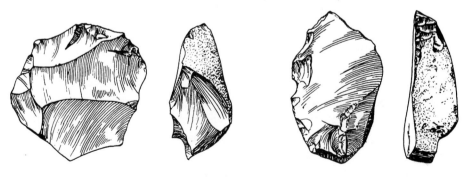

Fig. 66 Crudely worked flints from Hoxnian sediments at Clacton. These flints represent the earliest undisputed evidence of man in Essex, approximately 400,000 years ago. *(Illustration: J. Wymer)*

81

Terraces of the Thames

That part of a river valley over which a river flows in times of flood is called a **flood plain**. Over this area the river deposits a thickness of sediment which buries the floor of the valley to varying depths. The changes in climate during the Ice Age had an effect on the nature of the river and periodically the river cut down through the sediment leaving fragments of the former flood plain abandoned at a higher level. Further deposition of sediment created a new flood plain and as this cycle continued a series of bench-like **terraces** were created at each side of the valley, the oldest being at the highest elevation.

The present (post-diversion) Thames and its tributaries have a number of terraces, each terrace being formed by a deposit of gravel and also a silty loam called **brickearth**. A brickearth or **loess** is a fine-textured deposit which probably originated as a dust blown southwards by winds from an ice sheet and redeposited by water. The dating of these terraces in different parts of the present Thames valley has proved difficult because of their varying heights and the fact that much has been removed by subsequent river erosion.

The oldest and the highest of the Thames terraces is represented only by isolated remnants along the modern Thames valley. During excavations for a railway cutting at Hornchurch in the nineteenth century, these old terrace gravels were found to be lying on a remnant of boulder clay (known as the Hornchurch Till) which was deposited at the southern-most extremity of the Anglian ice sheet. Hornchurch is therefore an important site for showing that the present Thames valley was formed after the Anglian glaciation.

Middle terraces, which form more extensive deposits than the high terrace, contain bones of large mammals. Many famous sites yielded mammoth and other spectacular fossils in the nineteenth century such as those at Grays and Ilford (see box) when brickearth was being worked for making bricks. Also associated with middle terrace deposits are interglacial sediments channelled into the London Clay at Aveley which yielded bones of a mammoth and a straight-tusked elephant in a clay pit in 1964 and the first fossil found in Britain of a jungle cat in a nearby road excavation in 1997 (see box). From evidence at Aveley and elsewhere it is clear that this stage of the Ice Age, known as the **Wolstonian**, is a complex glacial/interglacial sequence that is not yet fully understood. In fact, the name 'Wolstonian' may even be invalid as it has been suggested that the glacial sequence at the site after which it has been named (Wolston in Warwickshire) is of Anglian age.

During the latter part of the most recent (Devensian) glacial stage (about 25,000 years ago) sea level fell to a very low level and the Thames cut a deep channel below the present estuary extending out across a landscape that now lies below the southern North Sea. This channel still exists but is now completely filled with sediments. Dating from this period are terrace deposits in the Lea valley which have yielded mammoth, woolly rhinoceros, reindeer and beds containing arctic plants.

The terraces of the present Thames have provided London with flat land for development. The 'Flats' of East London are good examples of terrace surfaces; Leyton Flats is a fragment of the high terrace and Wanstead Flats a part of one of the middle terraces.

The terraces of the modern Thames valley have been scientifically studied for more than a century but in 1992 news of the discovery of 'pre-diversion' Thames terraces in Essex was published. Evidence from boreholes and gravel pits between Harlow and Clacton has revealed at least eight terraces within the Kesgrave Sands and Gravels (page 64), now almost entirely buried by boulder clay. Correlation of these terraces with those of the Thames upstream of London will finally enable us to unravel the complex history of this great river.

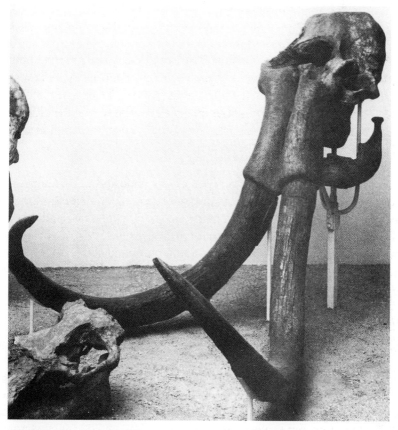

Fig. 67 The skull of the Ilford mammoth. Discovered in 1863, it is still the largest complete mammoth skull to have been found in Britain. The tusks are nearly 3 metres (10 feet) long. *(Photo: Natural History Museum)*

The Mammoth Graveyard

In the 1850s, when Ilford was a village on the London Road, a number of brick pits were in operation in the vicinity and occasionally the workmen came across the bones of large mammals in and below the brickearth. As the years went by the number of fossils found increased and they eventually came to the attention of Stratford amateur geologist Sir Antonio Brady. The pits were subsequently to produce an enormous number of specimens, all excavated under Brady's supervision, but the greatest moment came in 1863 when the skull of the 'Ilford mammoth' was unearthed (fig. 67) which had tusks nearly 3 metres (10 feet) long. Associated with it were the bones of a woolly rhinoceros.

Brady, a senior civil servant, devoted considerable time and money to ensuring that all the finds were preserved, and his collection was finally donated to the Natural History Museum in London. The collection contained the bones of more than 100 mammoths and at least 77 rhinoceroses. There were also bones of straight-tusked elephant, lion, brown bear and the giant deer *Megaloceros*, the span of whose antlers was a remarkable 3 metres (10 feet). A catalogue of the collection was published by Brady in 1874 and a copy is preserved in the Essex Record Office in Chelmsford. The catalogue records in great detail the excavation of the 'Ilford mammoth' and describes how difficult the task was. It states: 'You must imagine the skull resting half exposed in compact brickearth, requiring a spade or trowel to remove it, but the fossil itself as friable as decayed wood or tinder, the ivory of the tusks being equally soft and shattered.'

The reason for the remarkable abundance of fossils is not known but it is likely that they were carried by river currents to be redeposited in the quiet waters of a meander.

The Uphall Pit, on the west side of what is now Ilford Lane, was the most famous locality but there were others to the north and south of Ilford High Road. During their working life the pits received many visits from naturalist societies, one of which was reported in the Transactions of the Essex Field Club of 1880 under the title 'A day's elephant hunting in Essex'. All the pits have now been filled in and the sites developed. Fossil bones do, however, still occasionally come to light at Ilford; in 1984 bones of mammoth, ox and rhinoceros were discovered during construction of the Ilford Southern Relief Road.

The age of the fossils is still controversial (they are too old for radiocarbon dating and too young for the other radiometric dating methods), and fossils from the two main pits may be from different Thames terrace deposits; but they are probably between 150,000 and 200,000 years old.

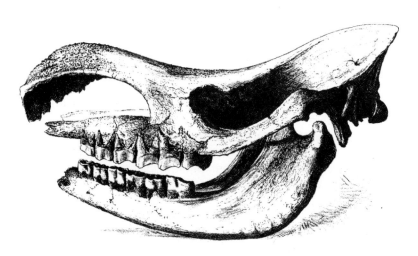

Fig. 68 The skull of a woolly rhinoceros from the Ilford brick pits.
An illustration from the catalogue of the Brady collection, published in 1874.
(Reproduced by courtesy of the Essex Record Office)

Fig. 69 The discovery of mammoth and other fossils at Ilford in the nineteenth century is commemorated by a plaque on the wall of Ilford Methodist Church in Ilford Lane. *(Photo: G. Lucy)*

Two Elephants and a Jungle Cat

In 1964 an amateur fossil collector, John Hesketh, discovered a number of large bones in a clay pit then being worked by the Tunnel Portland Cement Company Ltd. on the north side of Sandy Lane, Aveley. These finds were brought to the attention of the Natural History Museum in London and soon afterwards a team began a major excavation of the site, which received much publicity in the national press. The excavation revealed two skeletons, one lying almost on top of the other; the upper one was of a mammoth preserved in a seam of peat, and the lower one of a straight-tusked elephant preserved in silty clay.

The mammoth may be younger than the straight-tusked elephant, their close proximity due to them having been trapped in the same soft marshy ground, apparently a silted-up channel, at different times. The sediment beneath the mammoth was found to be disturbed, probably due to the animal struggling to escape. The skeletons were removed still partly embedded in a large block of sediment, which is now in the Natural History Museum in London.

Over thirty years later, in 1997, a nearby road cutting for the A13 exposed the same sediments and Aveley again found itself with nationwide press coverage. The reason this time was the first discovery in Britain of the bones of a jungle cat, an animal that today lives in China, Central Asia and Egypt. The Daily Telegraph, in particular, covered the story well with the front page headline 'Mother of the modern moggie found in Essex'. With the jungle cat were the bones of six species new to Aveley including a brown bear and a very large lion.

Mother of the modern moggie found in Essex

THE ancestor of the domestic cat stalked Essex 200,000 years ago, according to palaeontologists after the discovery of jungle cat remains in Britain, writes Roger Highfield, Science Editor.

Fossilised bones of *Felis chaus* were uncovered during a dig along the A13 at Aveley, Essex, on what were the banks of the Thames.

The remains of many other mammals, including a larger version of today's lion, have also been preserved in silt.

Essex bore closer resemblance to the African savannah of today during the Pleistocene period, which was a relatively warm era between ice ages. The jungle cat, larger than a

The jungle cat also lived here

modern wild cat but smaller than a lynx, has a short tail and tufted ears. It would have hunted small mammals, birds and frogs in the marshy area beside the river.

Danielle Schreve, a palaeontolo-

gist of Durham University, who is leading the dig, said: "It is a really exciting find because we had no idea this cat had ever reached Britain.

"Its normal distribution area is Egypt and central Asia. The ancient Egyptians first had the idea of bringing them into their houses."

The jungle cat is still found in the Nile delta and in central and south-east Asia.

Miss Schreve, 25, said: "This cat could easily have played a part in the ancestry of the modern kitty."

But the neanderthals in Britain at the time would not have domesticated it.

The cat likes marshy areas and the river would have been flanked by

enormous grassy plains and huge herds of animals. The vegetation was abundant, she said.

"Because of this, the grass-eating herbivores grew to a large size, so the carnivores that preyed on them had to be big to be successful."

Miss Schreve said the lions discovered near the cat are similar to those found in Africa today "but were about 30 per cent bigger".

The remains discovered comprise the creature's front leg — the humerus, radius and ulna bones — the longest of which is five inches.

The dig was sponsored by the Highways Agency and co-ordinated by the Field Archaeology Group of Essex County Council.

Despite the presence of mammoth, the fauna at Aveley indicates that the deposits were laid down during a warm interglacial stage (about 200,000 years ago). It appears that early mammoths tolerated the rising temperature and continued to live in southern England throughout this interglacial stage.

Fig. 70 The initial stages of the excavation of the Aveley elephants in 1964. In the background is the clay excavating machinery belonging to the Tunnel Cement Company, owners of the clay pit. *(Photo: A.J. Sutcliffe)*

Fig. 71 Geologists from the Natural History Museum working on the bones of the Aveley elephants. The excavations brought so many visitors to the site that staff from the cement company had to give up their spare time to control the crowds. *(Photo: Times Newspapers Ltd.)*

Other Ice Age Sites

One of the most important Ice Age sites in Essex is East Mersea which has not only produced Hoxnian interglacial fossils from an early course of the Thames/Medway river (page 65), but nearby a channel beneath the modern beach is filled with Ipswichian interglacial sediments associated with the River Blackwater containing the rare remains of hyaena and hippopotamus (see cover illustration). The thought of hippos wallowing in the Blackwater is difficult to imagine when collecting fossils on this often windswept part of the Essex coast. Hippopotamus is characteristic of the Ipswichian interglacial; it is not thought to have lived in Britain at any other time.

Another Ipswichian deposit, at Wrabness on the River Stour, yielded bones of elephant and mammoth at the beginning of the eighteenth century. They were described as "diverse bones of an extraordinary bigness" and the writer concluded that they were probably bones of elephants brought over by Emperor Claudius for use in his wars with the Britons. Ipswichian fossils can also be found at Walton-on-the-Naze and bones from here were the subject of the earliest recorded reference to fossils in Essex; editions of Camden's *Brittannia* (1610-1695) refer to the bones of 'giants' being found in the thirteenth and sixteenth centuries.

Correlation of such deposits with those of the Thames terraces is difficult, and much work centres on the study of small fossils; these can yield important information. Beetles, for example, are adapted to particular ecological niches and can therefore provide evidence of the climate at the time of deposition.

Another very important field of research is pollen analysis, which involves counting and identifying types of pollen found in a sediment so as to build up a picture of the vegetation in the area over a particular period in time. A notable example of the use of this technique has been the study of the laminated silts and clay at Marks Tey brickworks (fig. 73) which are thought to represent the bed of a lake that existed during the Hoxnian interglacial stage.

Apart from the River Lea, whose fossils have already been mentioned, few sites in Essex yield fossils from the Devensian glacial stage (the last glaciation in Britain), but a gravel pit at Great Totham a few years ago exposed a peat layer associated with the River Blackwater which contained bones of mammoth, reindeer and wolf. Devensian fossils do, however, turn up at Essex ports, having been trawled up from the floor of the North Sea by fishing vessels; during the nineteenth century fishermen augmented their income by selling them to collectors. They originate from a time when the sea level was much lower and the southern North Sea was dry land, but today they lie in water depths of between 20 and 50 metres (70-170 feet). Nowadays these fossils, which include fine mammoth tusks and teeth, mostly end up at Dutch and other foreign ports to the benefit of collectors on the Continent.

Fig. 72 A mammoth tusk found during excavations for a reservoir at Shelley, near Ongar in 1983. The clay in which it was found was formed on the bed of a glacial lake. *(Photo: Essex Chronicle)*

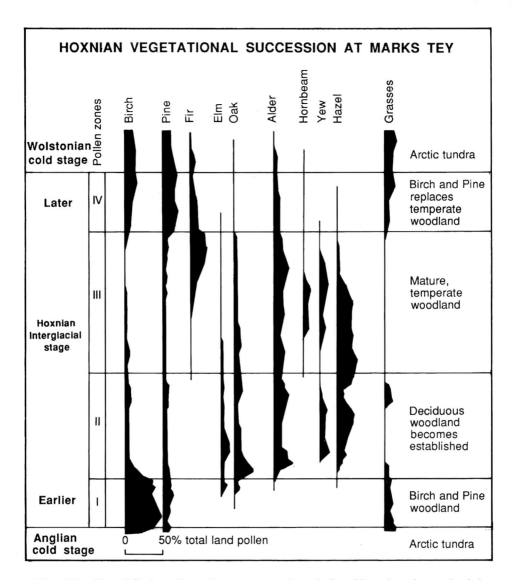

Fig. 73 Simplified pollen diagram produced for Hoxnian interglacial sediments at Marks Tey, near Colchester. *(Redrawn from Turner 1970)*

Analysis of pollen grains from sediments representing the bed of an ancient lake at Marks Tey has produced a remarkable record of the vegetation growing in this area over a complete interglacial cycle. The sediments at Marks Tey are laminated with distinctive layers caused by an annual influx of diatoms (single-celled algae) into the lake. Counts of these annual layers suggest a duration of approximately 25,000 years for the Hoxnian interglacial stage.

90

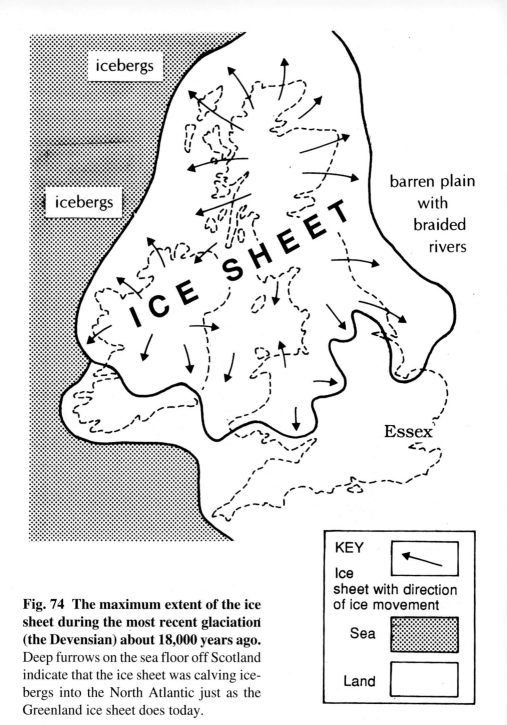

Fig. 74 The maximum extent of the ice sheet during the most recent glaciation (the Devensian) about 18,000 years ago. Deep furrows on the sea floor off Scotland indicate that the ice sheet was calving icebergs into the North Atlantic just as the Greenland ice sheet does today.

The Present Interglacial

The 10,000 years or so that have elapsed since the end of the last glaciation (the **Holocene** Period) is widely regarded as simply another interglacial period and is sometimes referred to as the **Flandrian** Interglacial.

A typical recent deposit is **alluvium** which is the name given to the silt and mud being deposited by modern rivers when in flood. It sometimes contains bones of mammals such as horse, elk, wild boar, bear and wolf as well as flint flakes and arrowheads made by man. The period of man's existence from the end of the last glaciation to about 5,000 years ago is called the Mesolithic (Middle Stone Age), and this was followed by the Neolithic (New Stone Age). The saltings of the Essex coast date from the Mesolithic to the present day.

The study of man, human artifacts, associated animal and plant remains and the sediments in which they are found are the archaeologists' field of interest. As the present is the key to the past, it is important for the geologist to study sediments now in the process of being laid down so that the conditions under which much older deposits were formed can be visualised. In this respect Essex is fortunate in having such a wide range of sediment types, reflecting different depositional environments, now accumulating along its coast.

The Next Glaciation?

We are still in the midst of the Quaternary Ice Age and when the next glaciation will come we do not know. However, there is evidence that the warmest period of the present interglacial was 5,000-7,000 years ago when sea level, which had been rising since the last glaciation, breached the land bridge with mainland Europe to make Britain an island again.

Recently, research has indicated that carbon dioxide emissions resulting from man's activities may have begun to affect this natural oscillation in world temperatures. There is evidence to suggest that the planet has already warmed by half a degree this century which compares with a rise of only 4°C at the end of the last glacial stage. If present rates of emissions continue, concentrations of carbon dioxide in the atmosphere by the middle of next century could be higher than at any time since the last interglacial, some 125,000 years ago, with disastrous effects on sea level and agriculture throughout the world.

Geologists a have vital role to play here in interpreting the evidence of the rocks and in this respect the sediments in Essex contain many clues to our changing climate.

Chapter 9

GEOLOGY AND ESSEX INDUSTRY

Economic Geology

Everything that we use that cannot be obtained by farming has to be dug out of the ground. An astonishing number of products that we use every day are derived from rock and Essex rock plays its part in providing us with these resources. Although the present economic rocks are predominantly sand and gravel this has not always been the case and there are many other geological formations which have supplied the raw materials for a large number of long-extinct industries.

Sand and Gravel

Sand and gravel for buildings and roads is of great importance and Essex possesses vast resources. Most sand and gravel quarries in the county are situated around Chelmsford and Colchester and a number of companies are involved in extraction. The gravels worked are of Pleistocene age and are usually those deposited by an ancient river system (e.g. the Kesgrave Sands and Gravels) but terrace deposits of present day rivers (e.g. the Blackwater and the Chelmer) have also been worked in some areas. They largely consist of rounded flint pebbles (originally derived from the Upper Chalk) but as we have seen in the previous chapter they also contain a proportion of 'exotic' rocks derived from distant sources. Some sands and gravels lie beneath a thickness of boulder clay which has first to be removed before extraction can proceed (fig. 52).

Moulding sand for brass casting and iron moulding was formerly dug at Billericay from the Bagshot Sands. These sands are particularly fine and were very suitable for this purpose. Thanet Sand has been worked at Linford, near Tilbury for the manufacture of building blocks.

Bricks and Tiles

Brick making was probably introduced to Britain by the Romans nearly 2000 years ago and their bricks, because of their durability, can be found re-used in the structure of many ancient Essex churches. The dimensions of Roman bricks vary but they can be recognised by their characteristic shape, being more like tiles than present day bricks. Following the departure of the Romans, brick making was not carried out again in Britain until the twelfth century; some of the earliest surviving examples of this non-Roman brickwork can be found in Essex.

The main geological formations in Essex that have been found suitable for brick making are the London Clay and various Pleistocene brickearths. In the nineteenth century virtually every town had its own brickyard but the greatest concentration of brickworks was at Grays which developed around the brick making industry. In 1804 about 500 men were employed digging the Grays brickearth to make bricks for Martello towers. In the late seventeenth century Daniel Defoe (author of *Robinson Crusoe*) owned and operated a successful brickworks at Tilbury.

At the present time only a handful of brickworks are in operation. The Bulmer Brick and Tile Company's brickworks at Bulmer Tye in the north of the county near Sudbury currently makes bricks from a sandy clay near the base of the London Clay mostly for renovating historic buildings. The bricks are hand-made in the traditional manner and coal is still used as the fuel in the kilns. At Marks Tey, near Colchester, a grey clay of Middle Pleistocene age is worked by W.H. Collier Ltd. in a small brickworks, and a brickearth associated with the Thames terraces is worked at Great Wakering, near Southend, by the Milton Hall Brick Company.

Most of the bricks used in Essex nowadays are, however, made in large brickworks in Bedfordshire, Cambridgeshire and Surrey from clays of Jurassic or Cretaceous age.

Lightweight Aggregate

A lightweight baked clay with a honeycomb-like texture was, until recently, manufactured at the ARC Leca works at High Ongar by a unique process. The clay aggregate had many uses including building blocks, hydroponics and as a fill for roadside drainage trenches. London Clay was used as the raw material and this came from a large pit adjacent to the works.

Cement

The large quarries in the Upper Chalk around Purfleet and West Thurrock are the visible signs of the Portland cement industry of the past in Essex but chalk is no longer worked in the county for cement manufacture. Clay, the other essential ingredient of Portland cement, is still worked in a large pit in the London Clay at South Ockendon (fig. 26) and piped as a slurry under the Thames to Kent where it is used in the giant Northfleet cement works.

Before the invention of Portland cement in 1850, 'Roman cement' was made in Essex from accumulations of septarian nodules washed out of the London Clay cliffs along the coast. Harwich was the main centre of this industry, where the nodules (known as 'cement stones') were excavated from the cliffs; later, when the supply of stone dwindled, dredging offshore was carried out to collect nodules that had accumulated on the sea bed. During the early part of the nineteenth century up to 500 men were employed in this industry at Harwich and the cement was supplied to all parts of Britain and northern Europe. Much of the external rendering known as 'stucco' used during the Regency Period was made from this cement. There was also a cement factory at Leigh-on-Sea and the collection of cement stones here, and at Harwich, caused great concern because of the effect it was having on the erosion of the cliffs. An interesting account of this can be found in volume 2 of the Victoria County History of Essex (1907).

Building Stone

Good stone for building is very scarce in Essex and many early buildings had to be constructed of whatever rocks were available locally. The commonest of these, especially in the north-west and south of the county, were flints; many flint buildings can be seen around Saffron Walden. Flint is not an ideal building stone as it is difficult to work and when freshly dug occurs in nodules of irregular shape; but it is extremely durable. For churches and other important buildings throughout Essex 'knapped' flints were used (flints skilfully worked to produce a flat face) and fine examples of this craftsmanship can be seen on the fifteenth century gatehouses of St. John's Abbey, Colchester, and St. Osyth's Priory, near Clacton. The best quality flint, however, probably did not come from Essex, but from Brandon in Suffolk, an area where flint has been mined since the Stone Age. The construction of round church towers (there are six in Essex) came about because of the difficulty of making satisfactory corners with natural unknapped flints. One of these churches can be seen at South Ockendon.

Septarian nodules (also known as 'septaria') from the London Clay can be seen in old buildings in east Essex, particularly churches close to the coast. The Romans used septarian nodules extensively (a surviving example being Colchester's Roman wall) but probably the best example of the use of this stone is the Norman castle at Colchester (fig. 78).

In north and west Essex there are churches constructed of Hertfordshire puddingstone, sarsens and other erratics and in the east there are churches built from blocks of **ferricrete** (an iron-cemented sand or gravel) which makes a remarkably good building stone. The best example of the latter is the church at Great Bentley, near Colchester. The types of stone used in the fabric of a church can be a valuable guide to the age of the building.

Chalk is an unlikely material for building but at some horizons in the formation a harder chalk known as **clunch** exists which was quarried in the extreme north-west of the county. It was fairly soft when quarried and sometimes left for up to two years to dry out and harden sufficiently before use. Large amounts of this material have been used in the interior of Saffron Walden church and a magnificent carved clunch mantelpiece can be seen in Saffron Walden Museum.

Copperas

A little-known industry, formerly of great importance in Essex, was the copperas industry. It consisted of the gathering of pyrite nodules (known as 'copperas stones') from Essex beaches, where they had been washed out of the London Clay, and then allowing them to oxidise for several months in open vats, whereupon a solution of ferrous sulphate (green vitriol) was formed. This was an essential chemical for dyeing leather and cloth black and for making black ink. Women and children were employed to gather the nodules from the beaches and were paid in 'copperas tokens'. Old records show that over 230 tons a year were removed from the beach at Walton in the period 1715-1720. Daniel Defoe, in his *Tour through the Whole Island of Great Britain* (1724) noted: "At Walton, under the Nase, they find on the shoar, copperas-stone in great quantities; and there are several large works call'd Copperas Houses, where they make it with great expense."

A Walton copperas token.

Although Walton was a major centre for the industry it was also carried out at Frinton, Harwich, Wrabness and Brightlingsea. It died out over 100 years ago but evidence of it still survives, for example 'Copperas Bay' and 'Copperas Wood' at Wrabness. An interesting account of the industry is given in the booklet *Copperas and Copperas Tokens of Essex and Kent* by W.H. George (copy available for reference in the Essex Record Office).

Phosphate

The fossilised droppings or excreta of prehistoric animals are called **coprolites** and these are common in some sedimentary rocks. The phosphatic nodules within the nodule bed at the base of the Red Crag were originally thought to be coprolites and it was formerly given the name 'coprolite bed'. In Suffolk, these nodules were the basis of an agricultural phosphate industry dominated, in the middle of the nineteenth century, by firms such as Fisons. In Essex, on a much smaller scale, these nodules were worked as a source of phosphate fertiliser at

Wrabness and Walton. Phosphate was an important U.K. industry before overseas discoveries were made.

Lime

Many farms on the boulder clay plateau of north Essex originally had at least one 'marl pit' for marling the soil. Good quality agricultural lime is now available from companies working large chalk quarries, one of which is Newport Limeworks (fig. 79). Although there is speculation as to their original purpose it has been suggested that the deneholes at Hangman's Wood near Grays and elsewhere were dug through the Thanet Sand into the Chalk for the same reason.

Lime was formerly in demand for building purposes and numerous lime kilns could be found, particularly where chalk was available as a raw material for firing. The only complete lime kiln that survives in Essex is at Beaumont Quay, near Thorpe-le-Soken.

Water

Water supply for villages and towns in Essex was formerly obtained from numerous local wells and boreholes driven into water-bearing rocks at various depths. The Chalk is permeable and rain falling on the outcrop passes down to form a vast underground reservoir of water known as an **aquifer**. The Chalk aquifer is still an important source of the county's water supply; the Tendring Hundred Water Company, for example (which serves the north-east corner of Essex), currently obtains 70% of its supply from borehole sources.

Water from wells and natural springs was, in parts of Essex, thought to have medicinal value and in the eighteenth and nineteenth centuries many towns became noted for their spas. The most famous of these was probably Hockley Spa (where a spring issues from the base of the Claygate Beds) and the pump room is still in existence today (fig. 80). It was opened in 1843 and as trade developed villas and an hotel were built for visitors. Christy and Thresh in their book *A History of the Mineral Waters and Medicinal Springs of Essex* (1910) tell of a woman being employed to dispense the waters "whose strong, healthy appearance visitors were led to believe was a result of the medicinal effects of the water". However, despite this, the enterprise did not succeed and "the public withheld its patronage and refused to be cured."

One of the most successful Essex spas was at Dovercourt (fig. 81) where a fine spa house was constructed in 1854 overlooking the sea. The water was described as 'chalybeate' (containing a high concentration of iron compounds) and was considered to be of high therapeutic value. The chemical compounds in spa water vary depending on the rocks through which it passes; each source therefore possesses a unique character.

There are records of at least 24 spas and medicinal wells in Essex; although some of these were very fashionable during the reign of Queen Victoria, the industry died out during the early years of this century.

Flint

The making of primitive tools from flint by Stone Age man must be the most ancient industry in Essex. Large numbers of such tools have been found throughout the county (figs. 64 and 66). Flint was also used for the manufacture of gun flints which was carried out at Purfleet up to the middle of the last century when flintlock weapons were finally superseded by those with percussion locks. Another industry was the calcining of flint which formerly took place at West Thurrock to supply the potteries at Stoke-on-Trent.

Salt

The extraction of salt is a very ancient industry. The Romans are known to have recovered salt at many sites on the Essex coast by evaporating sea water in large shallow dishes of baked clay. The visible signs of this industry are the 'red hills' that can be seen along the estuaries; these were formed from an accumulation of red soil which was a by-product of the fires used to apply heat to the salt pans. Salt is still produced at Maldon by the Maldon Sea Salt Company.

Fig. 75 London Clay being dug by hand at Bulmer Brickworks, about 1910.
(Photo provided by Adrian Corder-Birch)

98

Fig. 76 Nineteenth century bottle kilns at Marks Tey brickworks.
(Photo: G. Lucy)

Fig. 77 The giant Tunnel Cement Works, West Thurrock in 1963. The working chalk face can be seen in the distance and the Dartford Tunnel approach road is in the foreground. The works closed in 1976 and the site is now occupied by the Lakeside shopping complex. *(Photo: RTZ Estates Ltd.)*

Fig. 78 The Norman castle at Colchester is constructed mostly of septarian nodules from the London Clay. *(Photo: G. Lucy)*

Fig. 79 Newport limeworks in the north of the county.
The only working chalk quarry in Essex. *(Photo: G. Lucy)*

Fig. 80 The former pump room of Hockley Spa. Built in 1842, the building can still be seen today. Hockley was perhaps the most famous of Essex spa towns in the nineteenth century. *(Photo: G. Lucy)*

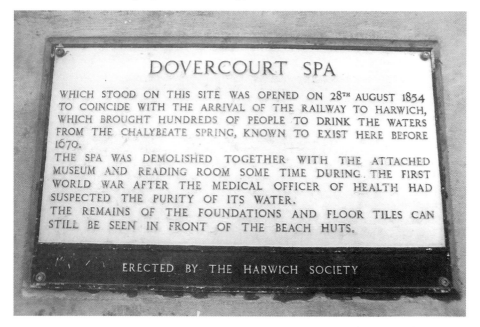

DOVERCOURT SPA

WHICH STOOD ON THIS SITE WAS OPENED ON 28TH AUGUST 1854 TO COINCIDE WITH THE ARRIVAL OF THE RAILWAY TO HARWICH, WHICH BROUGHT HUNDREDS OF PEOPLE TO DRINK THE WATERS FROM THE CHALYBEATE SPRING, KNOWN TO EXIST HERE BEFORE 1670.
THE SPA WAS DEMOLISHED TOGETHER WITH THE ATTACHED MUSEUM AND READING ROOM SOME TIME DURING THE FIRST WORLD WAR AFTER THE MEDICAL OFFICER OF HEALTH HAD SUSPECTED THE PURITY OF ITS WATER.
THE REMAINS OF THE FOUNDATIONS AND FLOOR TILES CAN STILL BE SEEN IN FRONT OF THE BEACH HUTS.

ERECTED BY THE HARWICH SOCIETY

Fig. 81 A plaque on the site of Dovercourt Spa, Harwich. *(Photo: G. Lucy)*

GEOLOGICAL FIELDWORK
AND CONSERVATION

Geology is essentially an outdoor subject, and although much can be learnt from textbooks there is no substitute for the study of rocks in the field. However, increasing interest in the subject over the last few years has led to a dwindling number of sites being more frequently visited by more and more people.

It was with this in mind, and to preserve irreplaceable geological sites for future generations to enjoy, that the Geologists' Association produced a *Geological Fieldwork Code*. The following 10 points, based on the Code, are applicable to Essex, and should be observed when visiting a geological site:-

1   Obey the Country Code, observe local bylaws, remember to shut gates and leave no litter.

2   Always seek prior permission before entering private land.

3   Do not interfere with machinery.

4   Wear eye protection and take care when breaking rocks, especially nodules of flint.

5   Avoid undue disturbance to wildlife. Plants or animals may inadvertently be displaced or destroyed by careless actions.

6   On coastal sections, be sure you know the local tide conditions and beware of intertidal mud.

7   Keep collecting to a minimum. Avoid removing fossils, rocks or minerals from a cliff face unless they are genuinely needed for serious study.

8   In working quarries or clay pits the leader of any party should be familiar with the current state of the quarry and should have consulted with the manager as to where visitors may go and what hazards should be avoided. On each visit both arrival and departure should be reported.

9	Suitable clothing and stout boots should be worn. Safety helmets are essential in quarries.

10	Foster an interest in geological sites and their wise conservation. Help to preserve a disused clay pit or quarry which may not only be of geological interest but also a haven for wildlife, and evidence for a long-forgotten industry.

A free copy of the full Geological Fieldwork Code can be obtained by sending a stamped addressed envelope to the Geologists' Association (details in Appendix C).

Earth Heritage Conservation

Geological sites are not only threatened by careless actions on the part of individuals but also by roadworks and development. The use of disused quarries and clay pits for refuse disposal also obscures all geological interest together with the value of the site as a wildlife refuge. Many important geological sites are, however, given some protection by being listed as Sites of Special Scientific Interest (SSSIs) by English Nature (the Nature Conservancy Council for England). There are 25 SSSIs in Essex which have been designated because of the importance of their geology or geomorphology. Some of these are listed in Appendix B.

Other geological sites, although they may be of local importance, receive no such protection and it has been up to the vigilance of local societies and individuals to ensure that they remain undamaged. Some years ago English Nature started a scheme to encourage the voluntary protection of such sites by land owners, local councils and societies which involves the setting up of a group with responsibility for designating Regionally Important Geological Sites (RIGS). Unfortunately, Essex does not currently have an active RIGS group.

Isolated glacial erratics are another important part of our heritage and may also be of archaeological interest as evidence for ancient trackways. In the last few decades many of these boulders have become buried in undergrowth or soil and relocating them is a fascinating and useful task. With practice it is easy to distinguish between these natural Essex boulders and the foreign boulders often imported nowadays for landscaping schemes.

The loss of geological sites, whether they are quarries, cliffs, boulders, or other natural features, means a loss of local identity and an erosion of not only the scientific but also the cultural and historical interest of an area.

Useful illustrated leaflets on earth heritage conservation are available free of charge from English Nature (01733 455101).

Appendix B

SOME PLACES OF
GEOLOGICAL INTEREST IN ESSEX

Not all of the sites here described are easily accessible but they have been selected to represent the many different aspects of Essex geology. It must be stressed that many are on private land and **under no circumstances should they be entered without first obtaining permission from the landowner**. This also applies to the working quarries and clay pits.

Some sites have been designated as 'Sites of Special Scientific Interest' (SSSIs) on account of their geological interest and therefore have statutory protection. On any site the geological code of conduct (Appendix A) should be adhered to at all times.

Alphamstone (TL 879355)
At least nine large sarsen stones can be seen in and around the churchyard of St. Barnabas church.

Althorne, The Cliff SSSI (TQ 922967)
A cliff on an outer bend of the River Crouch near Burnham-on-Crouch is being eroded and London Clay fossils, although scarce, can sometimes be found in the beach shingle below the cliff (fig. 38). Selenite (gypsum) crystals can also be found on the beach, washed out of the clay.

Arkesden
A number of giant puddingstone boulders can be seen in the bed of the stream by the bridge in the centre of this pretty Essex village; others can be found by the inn and in gardens nearby. The war memorial in the churchyard consists of a single block of puddingstone. The gently rolling countryside in this part of Essex is typical chalk landscape and is the highest ground in the county. The highest point in Essex is actually in High Wood, some 3 kilometres (2 miles) north-west of Arkesden and is approximately 140 metres (460 feet) above sea level. All of these valleys are now dry (due to the permeability of the Chalk) and so they must have been formed by fast-flowing rivers when the ground was frozen to a considerable depth during the coldest periods of the Ice Age.

Asheldham
A glance at the 1:50,000 scale Ordnance Survey map of the Colchester area reveals a line of flooded gravel pits stretching across the Dengie peninsula from Burnham-on-Crouch to Bradwell. This was the route of the Thames/Medway

river (fig. 51) and the gravel it deposited is known as the Low Level East Essex Gravel. One of these pits, at Asheldham (TL 974018), is now a delightful Essex Wildlife Trust nature reserve where iron-stained gravel and sand are sometimes visible in the degraded banks. Digging is not, of course, permitted. On the other side of the road is a commercial gravel quarry which can be viewed from the adjacent footpath.

Aveley
Disused clay pits near Aveley formerly exposed the lower divisions of the London Clay. The pits are all private and used as landfill sites.

Ballingdon (TL 860405)
A large, private disused quarry on the Essex/Suffolk border near Sudbury with fine exposures of Upper Chalk and Thanet Sand. The floor of the quarry is occupied by an oil storage depot.

Braintree
In front of the museum in Manor Street is a statue of John Ray, the naturalist (1627-1705). Although he is chiefly known for his work in botany and zoology, he contributed greatly to the advance of geology, particularly with his observations on the origin of fossils. He is buried in Black Notley churchyard.

Bulmer Tye (TL 833382)
London Clay is worked here for making traditional, hand-made red bricks mostly for the renovation of historic buildings. The sandy clay in the small pit contains a layer of cement stone nodules and seams of volcanic ash.

Chelmsford
Working gravel quarries in the vicinity of Chelmsford expose boulder clay underlain by Kesgrave Sands and Gravels with London Clay visible in the quarry floors. Many unusual rocks and fossils can be found in the boulder clay and pieces of silicified fossil wood and puddingstone occur in the gravels. The largest of these quarries is at Bulls Lodge Farm at Boreham, north-east of Chelmsford, and this is likely to become the biggest sand and gravel processing operation in the country. At Chelmsford Museum a block of puddingstone stands next to the main entrance door.

Colchester
The fifteenth century gatehouse of St. John's Abbey is a fine example of the use of knapped flints known as 'flushwork'. Colchester Castle and much of the Roman wall is made of septarian nodules from the London Clay, probably gathered from the Essex coast. In the suburb of Greenstead, an unusual sarsen stone stands next to a bus stop at the southern end of Avon Way.

East Mersea SSSI (TM 068146)

One of the most important geological sites in Essex, the cliffs at Cudmore Grove provide superb exposures of Thames/Medway gravels laid down during the Hoxnian interglacial stage when monkeys, bears and early man lived in Essex. Beneath the beach gravel, and inaccessible, are channel deposits from the more recent Ipswichian interglacial stage which have yielded bones of hippopotamus, elephant, rhinoceros and hyaena.

Fig. 82 The cliffs at Cudmore Grove, East Mersea. *(Photo: G. Lucy)*

Elsenham (TL 550265)

London Clay is sometimes exposed at the base of this working gravel quarry, overlain by Red Crag, Chillesford Sand, Kesgrave Sands and Gravels (mostly sands), and chalky boulder clay. The Red Crag here does not contain fossils as they have been dissolved by percolating ground water.

Fingringhoe (TM 045195)

Fingringhoe Wick was a working gravel quarry between 1924 and 1959. It is now one of the finest nature reserves in Essex and the headquarters of the Essex Wildlife Trust. Visible on the far side of the lake and elsewhere are mounds and banks of glacial sand and gravel deposited by torrents of meltwater issuing from the ice front when it was situated only some 12 kilometres (8 miles) west of here (fig. 51). From the edge of the reserve there are fine views of the Colne estuary.

Grays

There are many large quarries in the Upper Chalk in the vicinity of Grays and Purfleet (fig. 17). In some, Thanet Sand and Thames terrace gravels can be seen overlying the Chalk, for example at Mill Wood (Gibbs) pit, west of Mill Lane in South Stifford which has excellent exposures. In others, vegetation has taken hold, providing a haven for wildlife such as the well known Grays Chalk Quarry SSSI west of Hogg Lane. Care should be taken (and permission always obtained) when visiting quarries. A safe alternative to study is a fine exposure of Thanet Sand and the top of the Upper Chalk that can be seen at the junction of Drake Road and Devonshire Road in the new Chafford Hundred development. Despite the apparent abundance of quarries, most of those remaining are threatened with development or landfill. Some fine sarsen stones can be found in the area; a particularly good example is situated at the front of Thurrock College.

Great Wakering (TQ 939872)

Although loess is common on the Continent, in Britain only in east Kent and here in south-east Essex are substantial thicknesses of this material preserved. Exposures of this brickearth are present in the disused and flooded workings to the east of Star Lane Brickworks. The workings can only be examined with prior permission from the landowner.

Hadleigh

The town of Hadleigh is situated on the Rayleigh Hills and is built on High Level East Essex Gravel which was deposited as a left-bank terrace of the River Medway when it flowed across eastern Essex to join the ancestral Thames. All of the pebbles in this gravel (including the sarsen stone built into a wall of Hadleigh Church) therefore originated in Kent.

Hadleigh Castle (TQ 810860) is on the edge of an old cliff line which was abandoned by the sea during the most recent glacial stage. An area of marshland has now developed in front of the degraded cliffs which are composed of London Clay overlain by Claygate Beds and Bagshot Sand. The cliffs are a good example of a rotational landslip and its effects on the castle can be clearly seen. Between here and Leigh-on-Sea the steps, paths and roads require regular repair because of landslipping. Low cliffs with landslips can be seen in Shipwright's Wood (TQ 796873), adjacent to the recreation ground in Shipwright's Drive. This fine and varied woodland has some Bagshot Sand visible around the eastern edge and lower down several springs issue from the junction with the Claygate Beds.

Harlow (TL 428090)

A giant boulder of puddingstone, probably the largest in Essex, stands upright in the quadrangle of the offices of Smithkline Beecham (formerly B.P. House) in Third Avenue. It was discovered during excavations in 1966.

Harwich SSSI (TM 263320)

The foreshore yields occasional London Clay fossils. Of particular interest is the Harwich Stone Band which contains attractive veins of calcite and also volcanic ash from explosive volcanic eruptions in Scotland and Scandinavia during Eocene times.

High Beach

The high ground around the King's Oak Inn is capped with gravel deposited by an unknown river that flowed north from the Weald of Kent to join the ancestral Thames (gravels of similar composition occur at the top of Shooters Hill in south London). Well-rounded pebbles from this gravel are revealed on the many footpaths hereabouts. Beneath the gravel is Bagshot Sand which is visible on the steeply-sloping paths to the north-west of the inn. Many similar high points exist such as Billericay, Havering-atte-Bower, the Langdon Hills and Warley.

High Ongar (TL 564025)

This important pit formerly yielded London Clay fossils. It is now a private landfill site.

Hornchurch SSSI (TQ 547874)

The railway cutting at Hornchurch is of unique importance, providing evidence of the maximum southern limit of the ice sheets in Britain and demonstrating that the present Thames came into existence only after being diverted by this ice. Access is only allowed with a permit from Railtrack. Digging is not permitted.

Langdon Hills (TQ 678865)

Similar to High Beach, the Langdon Hills are formed from an isolated remnant (an outlier) of Bagshot Sand and Claygate Beds surrounded by London Clay lowlands. The summit is capped with river gravel deposited by a northward-flowing tributary of the ancestral Thames. This is the highest point in this part of Essex.

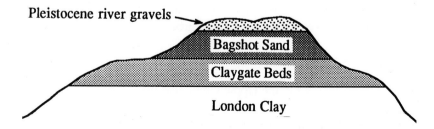

Fig. 83 The geological succession at Westley Heights, Langdon Hills.

Little Waltham (TL 724112)
At the entrance to Channels Golf Club is a boulder of puddingstone with a plaque commemorating the restoration of a nearby gravel pit. On the other side of the road is a large sarsen stone. Similar boulders can be found on the golf course.

Little Wigborough (TL 981146)
The delightful fifteenth century church of St. Nicholas was badly damaged in the 1884 earthquake. A brass plaque on the wall of the tower commemorates this event and the rebuilding of the church.

Marks Tey SSSI (TL 911243)
A clay thought to have been deposited in a freshwater lake during the Hoxnian interglacial period is worked in a largely overgrown pit for the manufacture of bricks.

Maylandsea (TL 907035)
Lobsters, sharks' teeth etc. can sometimes be found on the London Clay foreshore at low tide. Foreshore exposures at other sites along the River Blackwater yield similar fossils. Selenite (gypsum) crystals can also occasionally be found.

Newport
Newport limeworks near Newport station (fig 79) currently works Upper Chalk and there are usually fine exposures. In particular, there are good sections through numerous **solution pipes**: gravel-filled cylindrical pits formed by enlargement of joints by ground water. At the north end of the town, at the side of the road is a fine sarsen stone, known locally as the Leper Stone, and adjacent to this is a wall constructed largely of blocks of clunch. Outside the village hall in Station Road is a large block of puddingstone.

Orsett (TQ 655810)
A private quarry behind the Orsett Cock public house provides a fine exposure of Thanet Sand, Woolwich Beds and Thames terrace deposits.

Osea Island and Northey Island
London Clay fossils can sometimes be found on the foreshore at low tide. Warning: the islands can only be reached at low tide by causeways from the mainland.

Saffron Walden
Of the dozens of quarries in the Upper Chalk that used to exist in the north-west of the county only a few are still visible. The best of these is a private quarry situated in Saffron Walden behind the cul-de-sac known as Limefields on Little Walden Road within walking distance of the town centre. Numerous glacial

erratics are situated in the grounds of Saffron Walden Museum, including a three tonne septarian nodule. Large quantities of clunch were used in the interior of St. Mary's church.

West of Saffron Walden is Audley End House (owned by English Heritage) where there is a sarsen stone opposite the entrance gates. In the grounds of the house on the Tea House Bridge is a fine Jurassic septarian nodule sliced in half and used as a table. Inside the house is a nineteenth century collection of minerals and fossils which includes a mammoth tusk collected nearby in 1832.

The ploughed fields on the boulder clay plateau of north-west Essex are some of the best places to collect rocks and fossils. Wherever boulder clay lies below the surface (fig. 48), and the field is free of crops and rain-washed, numerous interesting specimens can be found. However, permission should always be obtained from the owner of the land.

South Ockendon (TQ 611833)
Fine exposures of London Clay can be seen in the large working clay pits at South Ockendon (fig. 26), providing clay for the cement works south of the Thames.

South Woodham Ferrers (TQ 813986)
Bushy Hill to the north of the town is of London Clay capped by Claygate Beds with landslips on the southern and western slopes. There are fine views from the summit with the Bagshot Sand hills of Rayleigh to the south and the Langdon Hills to the south-west. Less than a kilometre (half a mile) north of here is an isolated patch of boulder clay which indicates that a lobe of ice from the Anglian ice sheet briefly penetrated beyond Hanningfield to this point. To the east is typical London Clay landscape.

Stanway
The Kesgrave Sands and Gravels in the various working quarries here have, in the past, produced fine specimens of puddingstone, silicified fossil wood, chalcedony, carnelian and jasper, all due to the efforts of local amateur collector Bob Burton. In Stanway churchyard is the grave of the most famous Essex geologist John Brown (1780-1859), whose collection of nearly 8,000 specimens was bequeathed to the Natural History Museum in London.

Takeley
Between Takeley and Bishop's Stortford lies Hatfield Forest, 1,100 acres of medieval woodland owned by the National Trust. On the edge of the lake are a number of fine sarsen and puddingstone boulders. These were no doubt discovered when the lake was created in about 1750.

Vange (TQ 717874)

The long-disused Vange Hall brickworks pit has exposures of Claygate Beds. The sections are, unfortunately, overgrown and mostly obscured. The pit now forms part of the Basildon golf course.

Walton-on-the-Naze SSSI (TM 266235)

The Naze cliffs are an internationally important geological site with fine exposures of Red Crag and London Clay. The Red Crag and overlying sediments represent a remarkably complete sequence of late Pliocene/early Pleistocene deposits which have yielded information on climatic deterioration at the beginning of the Ice Age. Digging in the cliffs is not permitted but fossils are numerous in the slipped masses. The underlying London Clay is also fossiliferous and has produced some of the best preserved bird fossils of Tertiary age in the world. Sharks' teeth and pyritised fossil wood from the London Clay are common amongst the beach shingle. The London Clay also contains layers of volcanic ash. The Heritage Centre housed in the old lifeboat house in the town has a few fossils on display including some elephant bones of Ipswichian age found in 1995 during construction of a new breakwater.

Wendens Ambo

On the bend of the main road opposite the church is a high, ancient wall which is remarkable for the variety of local rocks used in its construction, including many large boulders. Although the pavement is narrow the wall provides an excellent opportunity to learn to identify different rocks, to see different rates of weathering, and to guess where the stones might have come from. The picturesque parish church of St. Mary, opposite, is largely of Norman age and here, like at so many Essex churches, much can be learnt about the age of the building from the rocks used in its construction. Information on this subject is contained in an article by J.F. Potter in Geology Today (see appendix D).

West Tilbury (TQ 656778)

The ridge of high ground between West Tilbury and Chadwell St. Mary is a high terrace of the present Thames and from here there is a view south over the Tilbury Marshes. The high point known as Broom Hill or Gun Hill is a rich habitat for animals and plants and adjacent to the road is a disused gravel pit with a small section through terrace gravels.

Wrabness SSSI (TM 172323)

London Clay cliffs on the River Stour in some places show conspicuous faults which are records of prehistoric earthquakes. There are also stone bands, veins of calcite, and layers containing volcanic ash. Nearby is an exposure of Pleistocene brickearth in which elephant bones have been found.

Appendix C

MUSEUMS, SOCIETIES
AND GUIDELINES FOR COLLECTORS

Museums

The finest geological collection in the region is at the Sedgwick Museum in Cambridge which is also a valuable source of advice. In Essex, Chelmsford, Harlow and Saffron Walden museums have purpose-built geology galleries. Many other Essex museums have good geological collections and some have specimens on display, notably Colchester Natural History Museum which has a display of Red Crag fossils and Southend Central Museum which has a display of London Clay fossils from the Essex coast.

Other museums within easy reach include Ipswich Museum (which has on display in the main gallery a full size replica of a mammoth complete with tusks and woolly coat) and, of course, The Natural History Museum in London which houses the national collections.

The Sedgwick Museum
Downing Street, Cambridge, CB2 3EQ.
Telephone: 01223 333456
One of the world's major collections of fossils. Museum staff are willing to help with the identification of fossils, and to advise on their treatment and care. A new mineral gallery has recently opened.

Chelmsford and Essex Museum
Oaklands Park, Moulsham Street, Chelmsford, CM2 9AQ.
Telephone: 01245 353066

Harlow Museum
Passmores House, Third Avenue, Harlow, CM18 6YL.
Telephone: 01279 446422

Saffron Walden Museum
Museum Street, Saffron Walden, CB10 1JL.
Telephone: 01799 510333

National and Local Societies

Essex Field Club
c/o The Department of Life Science, University of East London, Romford Road, Stratford, London, E15 4LZ
The Essex Field Club, founded in 1880, exists to promote the study of the county's natural history, and includes geology amongst its many activities.

Essex Rock and Mineral Society
c/o Fairkytes Arts Centre, Billet Lane, Hornchurch, Essex, RM11 1AX
The largest geological society in Essex with members throughout the county and beyond .

Geologists' Association
Burlington House, Piccadilly, London, W1V 9AG
Britain's largest association of amateur geologists with local groups throughout the country (including Essex).

Pudding Stone Study Group
c/o John Cooper, Department of Palaeontology, The Natural History Museum, Cromwell Road, London, SW7 5BD.
An informal group, founded to provide a forum for people with an interest in the scientific study and folklore of puddingstone and sarsen stones.

Rockwatch
The Green, Witham Park, Waterside South, Lincoln, LN5 7JR
A nationwide club for young people interested in rocks, minerals and fossils.

Tertiary Research Group
c/o Paul Jeffery, Department of Palaeontology, The Natural History Museum, Cromwell Road, London, SW7 5BD.
A society of amateur and professional geologists with an interest in the Tertiary period.

Guidelines for Collectors

A collection of rocks, fossils or mineral specimens can be both educationally and scientifically valuable; but only if it is arranged and looked after in the correct manner. Many amateur collectors in Britain own unique and valuable collections but they have only done so by learning to become skilled curators.

The following guidelines are included to assist collectors; they apply to any size of collection. The reader is also advised to consult the excellent books *Fossils Minerals and Rocks: Collection and Preservation* and *Geology and the Local Museum*, details of which are given in Appendix D. There is also a useful leaflet entitled *Rocks, Fossils and Minerals : How to make the best of your collection* published by the Geological Curators' Group; it is aimed at young enthusiasts and is available free from some larger museums.

1   The cleaning of specimens should be carried out with great care. Tap water and a soft brush are all that is usually required but with some specimens (e.g. chalk fossils) dry cleaning may be more appropriate. Specimens from the foreshore should be thoroughly soaked in fresh water to remove any salts.

2   Soft matrix adhering to a specimen can usually be removed with a knife but instruments such as dental tools are much more useful (if they can be obtained). The removal of harder matrix requires a small hammer and chisel and a degree of skill. Electric engraving tools can also be useful for this purpose. Remember to wear eye protection when carrying out this work. If a specimen is likely to be of scientific value, seek the advice of a museum or a geological society.

3   Fossils containing pyrite (e.g. London Clay fruits and seeds) are often very unstable and after thorough cleaning in fresh water should be dried and stored in air tight containers. There are a number of ways of treating such fossils to delay decomposition but many are costly and difficult. The important thing is to reduce the humidity inside the containers and this can be done by adding a bag of silica gel obtainable from photographic shops.

4   Under no circumstances should a specimen be varnished or otherwise treated to 'improve' its appearance. If treatment is necessary to consolidate a fragile specimen it should be carried out using a treatment which can be removed at a future date for retreatment. PVA adhesive (diluted with water) can often be used with some success and UHU adhesive is suitable for repairs. Fragile fossils from Ice Age sites (e.g. mammoth tusks) often present severe problems and advice should be sought from a museum or geological society.

5   Specimens should be provided with a label giving the exact locality where found (including the Ordnance Survey grid reference), the geological formation and the date of collection. In the case of fossils found in a cliff face the particular horizon (i.e. the position in the cliff or excavation) should also be given. It is important to note down this information **at the time of**

collection so that it is available when writing permanent labels at home. To note the name or species is of secondary importance as the specimen can always be identified at a later date. In the case of purchased specimens the date of purchase, price and name of the retailer should be given. Old labels may be of historical interest and should be retained.

6   Labels should be kept with the specimens and preferably attached to them if possible. The common practice of merely numbering specimens and recording the information in a catalogue is not recommended as the history of geological collecting is littered with instances where the collection has survived but not the catalogue. A catalogue is, however, very useful as a duplicate record and to give more information about a specimen and its locality.

7   The collection should be kept in a cabinet with close-fitting drawers in a cool part of the house with low humidity. If a suitable cabinet cannot be obtained an excellent alternative is a number of shallow cardboard boxes with lids. Each specimen should be contained within a card tray or plastic box lined with foam or tissue where necessary. Cotton wool is not recommended as it often adheres to specimens.

8   Try to specialise and so create a collection which will be of greater educational and scientific value. Collect from a particular part of Britain (e.g. Essex), or from a particular geological formation (e.g. London Clay).

9   Personally collecting specimens is the most satisfying method of obtaining them but do not rule out opportunities for purchasing or exchanging them to enhance your own specialist collection. Membership of a geological society will put you in touch with fellow enthusiasts.

10   Specimens which cannot be identified should be referred to a museum or geological society. Many specimens of scientific value have probably been lost to science because this has not been done.

Suppliers

Stuart A. Baldwin (Baldwin's Scientific Books)
Fossil Hall, Boars Tye Road, Silver End, Witham, Essex, CM8 3QA
Tel.: 01376 583502
Suppliers of geological books.

Evans Lapidary Machines.
54, Beesfield Lane, Farningham, Kent, DA4 0BZ Tel.: 01322 862252
Manufacturers of lapidary machinery.

Geo Supplies Ltd.
16 Station Road, Chapeltown, Sheffield, S30 4XH Tel.: 0114 245 5746
Suppliers of geological equipment.

GEOU
Department of Earth Sciences, The Open University, Walton Hall,
Milton Keynes, MK7 6AA Tel.: 01908 654871
Suppliers of replica fossils.

P&M Boxes Ltd.
32/34, Maple Avenue, Leigh-on-Sea, Essex, SS9 1PR
Tel.: 01702 478279
Suppliers of cardboard boxes with lids for storage purposes.

Fig. 84 A mammoth tusk found on the foreshore of the River Crouch.
Tusks and teeth of Ice Age mammals are usually very difficult to conserve and
expert help should be sought. This specimen, found by local historian Les Holden
(left) in 1983, was donated to Chelmsford Museum. *(Photo: Essex Chronicle)*

Appendix D

FURTHER READING

Geology and Scenery

Busbey, A.B. et al. **Rocks and Fossils: The Ultimate Guide to the Earth.**
　　Harper Collins. 1996.
Dixon, D. **The Practical Geologist.** Aurum Press. 1992.
Doyle, P., Bennett, M. and Baxter, A. **The Key to Earth History:**
　　An Introduction to Stratigraphy. John Wiley and Sons. 1994.
Dunning, F.W. **The Story of the Earth.** Natural History Museum. 1991.
Edmonds, E. **The Geological Map: An Anatomy of the Landscape.**
　　British Geological Survey. 1984.
Fortey, R. **The Hidden Landscape: A Journey into the Geological Past.**
　　Jonathan Cape. 1993.
Grayson, A. **Rock Solid: Britain's Most Ancient Heritage.**
　　Natural History Museum. 1992.
Janson-Smith, D. **Earth's Restless Surface.** Natural History Museum. 1996.
Roberts, J.L. **The Macmillan Field Guide to Geological Structures.**
　　Macmillan Press. 1989.
Whittow, J.B. **Geology and Scenery in Britain.** Chapman and Hall. 1992.

Rocks, Minerals and Fossils

Collinson, M.E. **Fossil Plants of the London Clay.**
　　Palaeontological Association. 1983.
Croucher, R. and Woolley, A.R. **Fossils, Minerals and Rocks: Collection**
　　and Preservation. Natural History Museum. 1982.
Fortey, R. **Life: An Unauthorised Biography.** Flamingo. 1998
Lister, A. and Bahn, P. **Mammoths.** Boxtree. 1995.
Natural History Museum. **British Caenozoic Fossils.** 1975.
Natural History Museum. **British Mesozoic Fossils.** 1983.
Pellant, C. **Rocks & Minerals** (Eyewitness Handbook).
　　Dorling Kindersley. 1992.
Rigby, S. **Fossils: The Story of Life.** British Geological Survey. 1997.
Rixon, A.E. **Fossil Animal Remains: Their Preparation and**
　　Conservation. Athlone Press. 1976.
Smith, A.B. (editor). **Fossils of the Chalk.** Palaeontological Assoc. 1987.

Sutcliffe, A.J. **On the Track of Ice Age Mammals.**
Natural History Museum. 1985.
Walker, C. and Ward, D. **Fossils** (Eyewitness Handbook).
Dorling Kindersley. 1990.

Regional Guides (Published by the British Geological Survey)

British Regional Geology : London and the Thames Valley. HMSO. 1996.

Geology of the Country Around: **Braintree.** HMSO. 1986.
Chelmsford. HMSO. 1985.
Epping. HMSO. 1987.
Great Dunmow. HMSO. 1990.
Southend and Foulness. HMSO. 1986.
Sudbury (Suffolk). HMSO. 1993.

Geological Maps (Published by the British Geological Survey)

1:625 000 scale (approx. one inch to ten miles).
Geological Map of the United Kingdom (south sheet)
(solid or drift editions).

1:50 000 scale (approx. one and a quarter inches to the mile).
205 Saffron Walden
206 Sudbury (includes part of Essex)
222 Great Dunmow
223 Braintree.
240 Epping.
241 Chelmsford.
257 Romford.
258/259 Southend and Foulness.
271 Dartford (includes part of Essex)

1:25 000 scale (approx. two and a half inches to the mile).
TL81 Witham.

Miscellaneous Publications

Baldwin, S.A. **John Ray: Essex Naturalist**. Baldwin's Books. 1986.
Bridgland, D.R. **The Quaternary of the Thames**. Chapman and Hall. 1994.
Bridgland, D.R., Allen, P. and Haggart, B.A. (editors) **The Quaternary of
the Lower Reaches of the Thames: Field Guide.**
Quaternary Research Association. 1995.

Christy, M. and Thresh, M. **A History of the Mineral Waters and Medicinal Springs of the County of Essex.** Essex Field Club Special Memoirs-Vol. 4. 1910.

Clifton-Taylor, A. **The Pattern of English Building.** Faber and Faber. 1987.

Cooper, J. (editor). **The Lost Trackway.** Pudding Stone Study Group. 1994.

Davies, W. **Catalogue of the Pleistocene Vertebrata from Ilford in the Collection of Sir Antonio Brady.** Private Publication. 1874.

Forrest, A.J. **Masters of Flint.** Terence Dalton. 1983.

George, W.H. **Copperas and Copperas Tokens of Essex and Kent.** Private publication. 1991.

Gibbard, P.L. **Pleistocene History of the Lower Thames Valley.** Cambridge University Press. 1994.

Haining, P. **The Great English Earthquake.** Robert Hale. 1976.

King, C. **The Stratigraphy of the London Clay and Associated Deposits.** (Tertiary Research Special Paper No. 6). Backhuys (Rotterdam). 1981.

Knell, S. and Taylor, M. **Geology and the Local Museum.** HMSO. 1989.

Meldola, R. and White, W. **Report on the East Anglian Earthquake of April 22nd 1884.** Essex Field Club Special Memoirs-Vol. 1. 1885.

Moorlock, B. and Smith, A. **S W Essex- M25 Corridor: Applied Geology for Planning and Development.** British Geological Survey. 1991.

Musson, R.M.W. **A Catalogue of British Earthquakes.** British Geological Survey. 1994.

Page, W. (editor) **Victoria History of the County of Essex.** Vol. 1 (geology) 1903 and Vol. 2 (industries) 1907.

Stuart, A.J. **Life in the Ice Age.** Shire Publications. 1988.

Wilson, C. (editor). **Earth Heritage Conservation.** Open University. 1994.

Periodicals

Down to Earth
Geo Supplies Ltd., 16 Station Road, Chapeltown, Sheffield, S30 3XH.
A quarterly newspaper for amateur geologists, free from most museums.

Geology Today
Blackwell Science Ltd., Osney Mead, Oxford, OX2 OEL.
A bimonthly magazine with news and views on all aspects of geology.

Earth Heritage
English Nature, Northminster House, Peterborough, PE1 1UA.
A twice yearly magazine on geological and landscape conservation.

Other Sources of Information

There are several hundred papers on all aspects of Essex geology that have been published in journals. Some of these are listed below.

• Allsop, J.M. and Smith, N.J.P. 1988.
The deep geology of Essex. Proc. Geol. Assoc. 99(4). 249-260.

• Anon. 1884.
In memoriam : Sir Antonio Brady.
Transactions of the Essex Field Club. 3. 94-101.

• Bridgland, D.R. 1988.
The Pleistocene fluvial stratigraphy and palaeogeography of Essex.
Proc. Geol. Assoc. 99(4). 291-314.

• Bristow, C.R. et al. 1980.
The Claygate Beds of Essex. Proc. Geol. Assoc. 91(4). 261-277.

• Ellison, R.A. 1983.
Facies distribution in the Woolwich and Reading Beds of the London basin. Proc. Geol. Assoc. 94(4). 311-319.

• George, W.H. 1997.
An Ipswichian interglacial site at Wrabness, Essex.
Essex Field Club Newsletter. No. 21. 4-6.

• George, W.H. 1997.
Prospecting for Pleistocene macro-mammalian remains at Walton-on-the-Naze, Essex in the nineteenth century.
Essex Field Club Newsletter. No. 20. 3-6.

• George, W.H. and Vincent, S. 1976.
Some river exposures of London Clay in Suffolk and Essex.
Tertiary Research. 1(1). 25-28.

• Hancock, J.M. 1975.
The petrology of the Chalk. Proc. Geol. Assoc. 86(4). 499-535.

• Hey, R.W. 1976.
Provenance of far-travelled pebbles in the pre-Anglian Pleistocene of East Anglia.
Proc. Geol. Assoc. 87(1). 69-81.

• Knox, R.W. and Ellison, R.A. 1979.
A Lower Eocene ash sequence in south-east England.
Quarterly Journal of the Geol. Soc. 136. 251-253.

- Mathers, S.J. and Zalasiewicz, J.A. 1988.
The Red Crag and Norwich Crag formations of southern East Anglia.
Proc. Geol. Assoc. 99(4). 261-278.

- Potter, J.F. 1987.
Geological traces of Saxon churches in the London basin.
Geology Today. 3(5). 164-168.

- Redknap, M. and Currant, A. 1985.
'Another day's elephant hunting in Essex' : recently excavated fossil remains from Ilford. Essex Journal. 20(1). 8-10.

- Roper, I.J. 1988.
The origin of chalky boulder clay - a provenance exercise.
Geology Teaching. 13(2). 84-86.

- Salter, A.E. 1914.
Sarsen, basalt and other boulders in Essex. Essex Naturalist. 17. 186-199.

- Turner, C. 1970.
The Middle Pleistocene deposits at Marks Tey, Essex.
Phil. Trans. Royal Soc. London. Series B. Vol 257. 373-440.

- Walker, H. 1880.
A day's elephant hunting in Essex.
Transactions of the Essex Field Club. 1. 27-58.

- Ward, G.R. 1978.
London Clay fossils from the M11 motorway, Essex.
Tertiary Research. 2(1). 17-21.

- Warren, S.H. 1924.
The elephant bed of Clacton-on-Sea. Essex Naturalist. 21. 32-40.

- Whiteman, C.A. 1992.
The palaeogeography and correlation of the pre-Anglian glaciation terraces of the River Thames in Essex and the London basin.
Proc. Geol. Assoc. 103(1). 37-56.

- Wire, A.P. 1890.
Essex Worthies. 1. Memoir of the late John Brown, F.G.S., of Stanway.
Essex Naturalist. 4. 158-168.

- Woodward, A.S. 1925.
Primitive mammals in the London Clay of Harwich.
Essex Naturalist. 21. 97-103.

INDEX

Page numbers in **bold type** refer to pages where the subject is dealt with in greater detail.

124

125

126

127

Valley Farm Soil 66
Vange 112
volcanic ash **41**, 106, 109, 112
volcanic rocks 9, 69
volcanoes 23, **41**, 46

Walton-on-the-Naze 5, 13, 14, 42-44,
  53-60, 88, 96, 112
Wanstead Flats 83
Warley 44, 64
Warley Gravel 64
water supply 97
Weeley borehole 21
Wendens Ambo 112
West Thurrock 94, 100
West Tilbury 112

whales 55
Wickham Bishops 12
Widdington 54, 68
Wivenhoe 13, 65, 66
wolves 88, 92
Wolstonian stage 62, **82**
wood: see fossil wood
woolly rhinoceroses 83-85
Woolwich Beds 15-17, 24, **32-33**, 35,
  36, 63, 110
Woolwich Bottom Bed 32, 40
Wrabness 43, 55, 88, 96, **112**

zones 9
zone fossils 9, 31